Animal
Heroes and Friends

Jean C. Keating

Astra Publishers
Williamsburg, Virginia

Library of Congress Catalog Card Number:
ISBN -13: 978-0-9674016-7-6

First printing, January, 2013
10 9 8 7 6 5 4 3 2 1

Astra logo by Beverly Abbott, For Arts Sake

Copies available from the publisher:
Astra Publishers
209 Matoaka Court
Williamsburg, VA 23185
(757) 220-3385
www.jeankeating.com

About the Author

Jean's life has been a life well-lived and one to be celebrated. While most people are grateful to have a career they love, Jean has been blessed to cherish not one, but three different and equally extraordinary careers. Jean laughed as she tossed back the thick tresses of her long, beautiful salt and pepper hair. "My first job was as a rocket scientist, working at NASA in Hampton, Virginia." A gleam in her eye indicates a subtle amusement as she refers to herself as a "rocket scientist." She was only 20 years old and had just gotten her Bachelor of Science in math and physics. "Because I had taken one course in astronomy, I was given a fabulous job in navigational astronomy. I was the first woman in the Control Center at Wallops Island on the eastern shore of Virginia, and I could sense my mere presence made the male engineers uncomfortable" Jean recalled. But the years were rewarding and productive. She discovered the positions of four stars to greater accuracies than previously known, was awarded a NASA special service award, received a personal letter of congratulation from the President and was named Virginia's Outstanding Young Woman of 1970 by the Outstanding Young Women of America Foundation. "We were launching suborbital rockets, a very exciting time at NASA." After ten years at NASA she resigned so she could stay at home and enjoy her newly purchased residence.

The second career began in 1973 when she went to work for the Council of Higher Education of the Commonwealth of Virginia. She was the Research Coordinator for 25 years. Over the years, she and her team developed a student data base with all the attending edits. Initially this model was used exclusively by Virginia colleges and universities. Eventually, however, the National Center for Education Statistics in Washington, DC, discovered the program. It was readily adopted, and now colleges and universities throughout the entire country report statistics using her system.

Her third career as a writer began shortly after she retired in 1998, and was born largely out of boredom. She had read every Agatha Christie novel ever written and decided it was time to write her own mystery. Her first book, *Amorous Accident* was based largely on aspects similar to her own life. The female protagonist is a NASA engineer, who discovers a murder while attending a dog show with her beloved Papillon, "Sky". Jean is an avid dog lover, and has raised and shown award winning Papillons since 1981. It was this book that led Jean to found Astra Publishers. Jean submitted *Amorous Accident* to two literary agents—both of whom liked the story, but wanted her to permit them to "make some changes". The first agent suggested Sky should be a Golden Retriever, "since a lot of people have never heard of the tiny Papillon breed" and the other agent wanted her to leave out the canine component altogether. Obviously, Jean rejected those suggestions—but she doesn't take "no" for an answer...Astra Publishers was the answer!

Jean has published six books, five of which were published by Astra Publishers: *Amorous Accident* and *Beguiling Bundle*—the first two of a planned mystery trilogy; *Paw Prints on My Heart* and *Paw Prints Through the Years*, a chronicle of Jean's life when, after a 19-year marriage ended in divorce, she began her life-long love affair with her precious Papillons; and *Love's Enduring Bond*, her most recent book, and her first attempt

at a writing a steamy, historical romance. The sixth book, *Published, Now Sell It*, was published through a publishing company in West Point, Virginia.
Written by Elizabeth Huegel

Also by Jean C. Keating
Amorous Accident
Beguiling Bundle
Love's Enduring Bond
Pawprints On My Heart
Paw Prints Through the Years
Published! Now $ell It

Dedication

This book is dedicated to Janet Abbott Fast, Publisher of *Chesapeake Style Magazine*, Michael and Dot Bryant, and Linda Lightfoot. Without their help, it would never have been possible.

Table of Contents

Monumental Courage
In late 2009, Virginians paid a long-overdue tribute to twelve gallant police officers who died in the line of duty. Grey skies echoed the somber mood of the large crowd of humans and canines who gathered on the grounds of the Virginia-Maryland Regional School of Veterinary Medicine at Virginia Tech in Blacksburg.

They came to pay homage to K-9 Baron, K-9 Bandit, K-9 Lobo, K-9 Zak, K-9 Sgt. Boris, K-9 Bodi, K-9 Iron, K-9 Colt, K-9 Faro, K-9 Ingo, K-9 Gunner, and K-9 Carsen. Between 1962 and 2008, these twelve dauntless and self-sacrificing K-9 officers paid the ultimate price for protecting the public and their handlers.

Until recently, their sacrifices received little notice. Just compiling the names of these heroes from newspaper files was extremely difficult. Then, six years ago, Deputy

John Hoover of the Franklin County Sheriff's Office and a master trainer with VA Police Work Dog Association began efforts to create a lasting memorial to their valiant contributions.

Funded totally through private donations, including a $40,000 gift from an anonymous donor, the memorial rests at the entrance to the vet school. It's a 110% scale

 model of a German Shepard Dog his right paw slightly raised, his shield proudly displayed from the collar about his neck, his ears alert and pointed outward across the Shenandoah Valley toward the Blue Ridge Mountains.

Hours before the dedication, the school's parking lot filled with officers and their dogs. Many walked quietly to the draped monument. Some to silently trace their fingers across one of the names engraved on the granite base, and then to walk away, brushing their eyes.

Blacksburg artist Larry Bechtel created the statue, called Ready to Serve, not only to honor the 12 fallen

heroes but also for the more than 250 dogs who serve throughout Virginia with state, local and college police units. On a large block of white marble in the walkway leading up to the monument is an engraving of the last line from a poem titled "I am a Working Dog" (author unknown) which poignantly reads, "So that you may live, my life is also yours."

Bechtel drew smiles from the crowd, which was heavily sprinkled with police uniforms representing units throughout Virginia and some from out-of state, when he spoke of his experiences with K-9 Boris, one of two dogs who now serve with the Virginia Tech police, who was his model. Bechtel wanted to examine Boris with his hands to determine anatomical relationships of features. Boris, Bechtel recalled, allowed the familiarity only after his handler insisted, but put his ears back to show he wasn't thrilled.

Five pipers and three drummers of the Virginia Highlands Pipes and Drums Band played *Going Home* and *Amazing Grace*. The Virginia Tech Corps of Cadets presented the Colors

William C. Mims, Attorney General of the Commonwealth of Virginia summed up the K-9 contribution in his keynote address. "When the public is in trouble, they call the police. When the police need help, they call S.W.A.T. And when S.W.A.T needs help, they call the K-9's." The uniformed officers nodded agreement.

When the group moved across the parking lot to reassemble around the monument, the area reverberated with the woofs of more than 70 police dogs. Many of the officers brought their dogs from their cruisers and formed a ring of honor behind the monument. Mims removed the drape and read the names engraved on the base of each fallen K-9, beginning with the earliest one.

K-9 Baron was killed on September 12, 1962 , beaten to death by an escaped inmate he was tracking in Powhatan. As Mims read his name, Baron's handler, Robert Coats, stepped forward. The 80-year old retired state trooper laid a white rose on the base of the monument as the pipes and drums carried the soft, haunting notes of Taps on the crisp mountain air.

Mims continued to read the name of each dog honored. With each name the dog's handler stepped forward and added a white rose to the floral tribute on the memorial.

Dr. Charles W. Steger, Virginia Tech President, noted that the first use of dogs in police work dates back to 1888, when London bobbies turned to the canine nose to track Jack the Ripper. It hadn't gone too well. One of the dogs bit the police commissioner.

But that kind of behavior isn't seen among Virginia's K-9 corps. One six-year-old girl was drawn to Officer D.S. Cressel and his 4-year-old GSD, Katie. The child had sold some of her toys to raise money for this memorial, and she asked politely if she might pet Katie. Cressel signaled Katie to sit and nodded his permission and the child threw her arms around the K-9 and kissed her on her ear. She was rewarded with a wet lick on her ear in return. Cressel said softly, "Katie loves children."

The attendees left to return to busy lives, and stillness descended on the memorial. Haunting words, snatches of a poem by an unknown author, seemed to echo across the lawn of the vet school.

Trust in me, my friend, for I am your comrade. I will protect you with my last breath.....I am a police working dog and together, we are the guardians of the night.

Born To Love, Trained to Serve, Loyal to the End, A Partner Faithful Beyond Words, They Gave Their Lives in the Service of Virginia

K-9 LOBO	K-9 INGO	K-9 CARSEN	K-9 SARGE II
10/10/83	10/24/04	12/12/08	9/25/80
NORFOLK POLICE DEPARTMENT	ALBEMARLE COUNTY POLICE DEPARTMENT	GILES COUNTY SHERIFF'S OFFICE	HAMPTON POLICE DEPARTMENT
K-9 ZAK	K-9 SGT BORIS	K-9 BARON	K-9 MAGGIE
3/19/93	2/13/96	9/12/62	12/12/11
NORFOLK POLICE DEPARTMENT	BRISTOL (TN) POLICE DEPARTMENT	VIRGINIA STATE POLICE	LOUISA COUNTY SHERIFF'S OFFICE
K-9 IRON	K-9 BODI	K-9 FREDDY/HR112	K-9 RED
1/30/97	7/26/96	10/28/09	11/06/11
NORFOLK POLICE DEPARTMENT	ORANGE COUNTY SHERIFF'S OFFICE	FEDERAL BUREAU OF INVESTIGATION	FRANKLIN COUNTY SHERIFF'S OFFICE
K-9 FARO	K-9 BANDIT	K-9 KING	
6/22/03	8/5/75	6/3/72	
NORFOLK POLICE DEPARTMENT	FAIRFAX COUNTY POLICE DEPARTMENT	AUGUSTA COUNTY SHERIFF'S OFFICE	
K-9 GUNNER		K-9 COLT	
6/6/05		6/25/00	
PRINCE WILLIAM COUNTY POLICE DEPARTMENT		CHESTERFIELD COUNTY POLICE DEPARTMENT	

Virginia's Fallen K-9 Officers

K9 Baron
EOW - 9/12/1962
K9 Baron of the Virginia State Police was killed when he was beaten to death by an escaped inmate he had been tracking in Powhatan, Va.

K9 King
EOW - 6/3/1972
K9 King of the Augusta County Sheriff's Office was shot and killed by a suspect during an open area search for the suspect. After K9 King had been shot once, he still tried to make an apprehension with the suspect and then was shot several more times in the chest.

K9 Bandit
EOW - 8/5/1975
K9 Bandit of the Fairfax County Police Department was shot and killed by the suspect he was pursuing.

K9 Sarge II
EOW - 9/25/1980
K9 Sarge of the Hampton Police Department was shot

by a barricaded suspect as he was trying to apprehend him.

K9 Lobo
EOW - 10/10/1983
K9 Lobo of the Norfolk Police Department was struck and killed by a vehicle while he was pursuing a suspect.

K9 Zak
EOW - 3/17/1993
K9 Zak of the Norfolk Police Department was killed during a "friendly fire" type incident during a building search for a suspect.

K9 Sgt. Boris
EOW - 2/13/1996
K9 Sgt. Boris of the Bristol, Tenn. Police Department was shot and killed by two carjacking suspects in Bristol, Va. K9 Sgt. Boris and his handler began tracking the suspects in Bristol, Tenn. and located the suspects in Bristol, Va. under a construction trailer. When he was deployed under the trailer to apprehend the suspects, he was shot and killed by the suspects.

K9 Bodi
EOW - 7/26/1996
K9 Bodi of the Orange County Sheriff's Office was shot and killed during a track and apprehension of a vehicle pursuit suspect.

K9 Iron
EOW - 1/30/1997
K9 Iron of the Norfolk Police Department was shot and killed by a fleeing home invasion suspect after he was deployed to apprehend the suspect.

K9 Colt
EOW - 6/25/2000
K9 Colt of the Chesterfield County Police Department was killed in a "friendly fire" type of incident while trying to apprehend a car chase suspect.

K9 Faro
EOW - 8/22/2003
K9 Faro of the Norfolk Police Department was shot and killed by a robbery suspect as he was trying to apprehend the suspect.

K9 Ingo
EOW - 10/24/2004
K9 Ingo of the Albemarle County Police Department was shot and killed by a burglary suspect after being deployed to apprehend the suspect.

K9 Gunner
EOW - 6/6/2005
K9 Gunner of the Prince William County Police Department was shot and killed in a "friendly fire" type of incident at the scene of a building search that was being conducted.

K9 Carsen
EOW - 12/12/2008
K9 Carsen of the Giles County Sheriff's Office was shot and killed in a "friendly fire" type of incident while conducting a building search in a church that had been burglarized.

K9 Freddy
EOW - 10/28/2009
K9 Freddy of the Federal Bureau of Investigation had

been stationed at Quantico, Va. He was deployed to Dearborn, Mich. where he was shot and killed in the line of duty.

K9 Red
EOW - 11/06/2011
K9 Red was with the Franklin County Sheriff's Office. K9 Red was struck by a vehicle while conducting a track of B&E suspects (first bloodhound in Virginia to be killed).

K9 Maggie
EOW - 12/10/2011
K9 Maggie was with the Louisa County Sheriff's Office. K9 Maggie was conducting a track of an armed suicidal subject when a loose pit-bull attacked Maggie. Maggie died from her injuries (first female dog killed in Virginia)

In keeping with police tradition, death dates of K-9 officers are shown above as End of Watch, EOW.

Editor's note: *Between the original 2009 publication date of Monumental Courage and the date of this book's publication, sadly five more names of fallen heroes have been added to the monument. All seventeen are listed above and shown in the photo of the monument.*

Jean C. Keating photos except close-up of names on monument, by Terry Lawrence

A Door into Sunshine

Hurricane season 2009 has brought gently falling rains to my yard. The soft grey of overcast skies and the soothing murmur of water falling on the car from the dwarf maple outside my front door make me a bit sorry that I've forsaken my bed so early.

"Yip! Woof! Arf," come from the throats of eight milling little bodies around my ankles. They're the reason I'm up at this hour. Eight tiny bundles of white and colored hair crowd in the doorway around my feet and then retreat back into the interior of the entranceway. None of the tiny furballs venture out the front door onto the wet walkway. In the first place, house rules forbid them going out the front unless specifically asked by me and then only if I'm out first. I'm not sticking my head out the door! I'm not interested in getting wet.

Which brings up the second reason the pack of little Papillons with whom I live aren't going out the front door. They aren't interested in getting wet either.

I retreat from the open doorway and close the solid door against the grey of early morning and falling rain.

"It's just as wet out the side door," I observe in a soft voice mixed with a chuckle. The pack pays my words no heed as all eight stumble over each other in their excited rush through the great room and kitchen, finally crowding through the laundry room to beat me to the side door. Jumping on hind legs and pawing me and the door in excitement, the pack eagerly await my fumbling with the lock to open the door anticipating their early morning foray into their large fenced area. Here, I generally walk around with them while they investigate all the smells and compare notes on which little bushy tailed friend (or foe) has dared to intrude during the night while they were asleep in the house.

Puff is the first through the side door as befits his status as alpha male of the pack. A large glob of water pouring off the roof line hits his shoulder and a steady downpour of rain in his face plasters the fringes on his big ears against his tiny head. He frantically shakes his head while he wheels and tries to return to the safety of the house only to collide with the bodies of Duke and Driver who are vying for position to be the second one into the yard.

The doorway turns into a churning jumble of bodies; dogs trying to get out blocked by and blocking dogs trying to get back in out of the rain.

"See. I told you." I laugh at their antics and gentle their agitation with my voice tones. I'm convinced the eight little canines understand a lot more of my language than most people credit them with doing.

Within minutes the entire mob has scurried outside long enough to get very wet feet, realize they're being drenched from the rain, and scramble back inside to weave around my feet. Thirty- two very wet and muddy little doggie paws wiped on white tennis shoes make a brown, yucky mess.

And no one has yet taken care of potty duties.

Nikki, the elder stateswoman of the pack, leads off back through the laundry room and kitchen, through the great room and into my study, where she stands expectantly by the outside door to the deck. The remaining seven papillons follow closely behind and are joined on their dash to the third door by a large Maine coon cat named Simba. I snag two large golf umbrellas as I slowly follow the expectant troupe.

"Crazy kids. I keep telling you it's wet out of all the doors." No matter. You can't avoid the hope that shines in all their eyes—or the need for an outdoor potty break even in the face of a downpour. A heavy sheet of water falling from the upstairs deck briefly checks their headlong dash out this third door. It gives me time to raise first one and then the second of the huge umbrellas and to get out the door ahead of the pack. Need mixed with curiosity brings first Puff, then the rest of the canines and finally Simba the cat outside on the wet deck hugging close to my feet and the questionable shelter provided by the umbrellas. Their dancing on first one foot and then another in silent complaint about wet paws from the soaked wood of the deck brings a smile even as I vocalize a gentle encouragement to follow me into the even wetter yard.

"Come on," I cajole, "you're really not going to melt from a little water."

Lured to the questionable shelter of the umbrellas, the milling bodies huddle around my feet in the yard until first one and then another venture into the falling rain, seeking limited cover under trees and shrubs in the yard. Eventually I'm left to myself under the umbrellas. I close one lest any early rising neighbors think me any more of a nut case than they already do.

Simba swipes at the tiniest of my dogs, Katie, when

she tries to wedge between him and the relative dry spot under a dense azalea bush. Both give me a look of disgust, signaling their jointly held belief that I am personally responsible for the soaked conditions.

The voices of two dedicated runners on the street draw the attentions of the dogs, and all eight rush to the fence line to challenge any possible intrusions into their yard, forgetting altogether the falling rain in their faces.

As the earth turns ever closer toward autumnal equinox, the colors in the yard other than green now come only from the white and ruby throated Rose of Sharon and three crepe myrtles in my own and the adjoining yards. Blossoms from the four scatter the yard and make for a pink, rose, lilac and white blanket of color as Simba and the eight, now-soaking wet dogs respond to my call to return to the house.

Four towels and a lengthy session with the hair dryer later, everyone is minimally dry and milling around in the kitchen demanding their morning treats.

Once nine demanding fur children have been satisfied with goodies, I finally have time to get myself a cup of coffee and turn on my computer, bring up my seventeen e-mail entries, erase the sixteen that are Spam, and answer the one of interest. Before I can open the file to the last page of my latest novel, Abby is at my knee demanding to be let out again.

And my friends wonder why it takes me so long to write anything! After all, I'm retired, aren't I!

Jean C. Keating photo.

A Writer's Life
I retired from my second career and decided to entertain myself with writing. After publishing my first novel, I was hooked, so more books followed. After the

fifth one won a national award, that got boring, so I decided to write a historical romance. After all, my critique group, mostly men, kept suggesting I needed to put more sex in my stories. So, I decided, a romance and one set in the period of the 1860's.

That's when my troubles began!

Now I think of myself as fairly knowledgeable about that period. I'm a civil war buff. I'm also a Papillon lover, breeder, and slave. My muse is a six-pound hearing assist service Papillon named Puff who usually provides the amusing stories that are subplots to my mysteries and accompanies me on book signings to pawagraph our books.

I told him he couldn't appear in my historical romance because Papillons did not come to the United States until the 1930's. I won't tell you what he thought of that. My editor wouldn't print it in the magazine.

So I set about writing my first historical romance. Now, for those of you who read such, the characters are always more beautiful/handsome than real life, and have extreme good and bad characteristics. But... and this is a big point...the historical part of the book is supposed to be accurate. That's why one reads the thing; to get a flavor of the times the romance depicts. Or so I thought. This being my first, I was not really sure. But I was trying to keep to accuracy.

So I told Puff his little antics wouldn't be depicted, and set out to portray the animal figure in my new literary masterpiece as a horse. Seemed appropriate! The male lead was a Confederate Colonel of cavalry. He's got to have a horse. It wouldn't make sense for him to be followed around by a six pound dog!

So I do an internet search on horse breeds and fall in love with a beautiful breed call an Andalusian. Big horses, usually 16 hands and taller, substantial necks, shoulders, hind quarters, intelligent, i.e. perfect for my cavalry colonel to be riding. Besides that, I just loved the sound of the breed name. Sexy, sensual on my tongue.

Sixty three thousand words later, the book is in final edit and an obscure internet note crosses my screen. It seems most Andalusians are cream or light in color.

Oh, great! Well, you can't very well have an entire company of cavalry, especially one called the Black Raven Company of the Black Horse Cavalry Regiment riding around on light or cream colored horses. So I just decided to ignore the fact that only five percent of Andalusians were black. This is, after all, a work of fiction.

As my two chief horse characters, Moosa and Shadow, did more and more endearing things in the novel, I decided that it might be a good idea to check with someone who actually knew the breed and ask for input as to the correctness of some of my action scenes involving the horses.

An e-mail to a Virginia breeder brought a warm and compassionate invitation to visit her farm and an offer to read the segments of my book pertaining to the horses. She provided much needed corrections to many points in the book.

"There's just one more problem", she gently said, in response to my query as to what else I should consider correcting. "Andalusians didn't come to the United States until the 1960's!"

After meeting two of her alluring and flirtatious Andalusian stallions, there was just no way I wanted Shadow and Moosa to be anything but Andalusians. So I decided to chuck the idea of historical accuracy and put that breed in my cavalry unit in my story of the 1860's.

After all, there is such a thing as literary license. I won't tell you what Puff had to say about this. My editor wouldn't print it anyway.

Jean C. Keating photo of Puff, and stallion owned by Jenni Coyle Johnson of JC Andalusians, LLC, Barboursville, Virginia

Animal Antics

In Isabel's wake, the last utility to come back on line at my house was the extended cable TV. I'd not realized how much I missed *Animal Planet* until I went without for three weeks. Happily among the first shows was a broadcast of the Texas dog show, and I caught the very end of the show when the judge was handing over the impressively large Best-In-Show ribbon to a beautiful Pekingese named CH Yankee Leaving Me BreathlessAtFranshaw. For those who would run out of breath before they could get that lengthy name out, he answers to Les. He makes a striking appearance, coupled with his tall, elegantly attired and handsome Hiram Stewart on the other end of his lead.

After so much devastation and property loss, so many property owners in shock at the monetary gap between insurance payments and outflow of money to remove, repair, and replace trees, roofs, windows, lawns, and decks, it was nice to sit back and watch Les and Stewart enjoy their big win. I was at Westminster in February, when the pair won the breed in Pekingese. Stewart was kneeling on the floor, his face awash with happy tears as he hugged the self-assured little bundle of fur that wagged his whole body in excitement. The *Animal Planet* coverage of the Texas show was a wonderful reminder that sometimes the simple things are those that mean the most to us all.

Life goes on in other parts of the country, as it will readjust and continue on here in Williamsburg. Neighbors and fellow citizens have exhibited wonderful patience and courtesy toward one another, as tree trunks and brush have lined every house, and blocked streets. They'd waited patiently and waved other drivers ahead of them at lights that failed to function or were erratic. The dratted storm brought a lot of negative things, but it also resulted in a return of community spirit and caring that have been a sad casualty of our increasingly hectic lives.

Tomorrow I'll worry about the ruined lawn, the fallen trees, the crushed flower pots. Les and Stewart remind me that the things that really count are the little fur children that sit close beside me on the sofa, safe, warm, and happy to be watching the other dogs parade across the TV.

Jean C. Keating

Autumn Memories

Finally! The temperatures have dropped to a seasonal crispness so that I am comfortable in my slipper socks, rumpled knit slacks and a long sleeved mock turtleneck

sitting in front of the fireplace with my feet up and pointed toward a warm and cheery blaze. Time was when the fire was wood-burning and I loved the crackle and smell of seasoned oak and pine logs. But seventy year old knees and a creaky back no longer afford the woman-power to clean and haul ashes and fresh wood. Gas logs and a smart thermostat supply the fire now. A lighted candle of wood scents provides some of the missing aspects. I'm content with the compromise. Growing old gracefully is all about enjoying today and being happy with what you have.

I glory in my memories of late falls in previous years—slipping down snow covered ski slopes or exploring the brilliantly colored woods on my horse. My skills at horseback riding and skiing were sub par, and I spent a lot of time taking jumps without the horse and landing on my rump or tumbling down the slope with my skis pointing skyward and in different directions. I enjoyed the adventure, even if I did think—as all do in their youth—that I was indestructible. Georgia Doll, my Morgan trail horse, long ago left for gentle pastures in the sky, my riding and skiing gear have long since been given away, and I'm left with wonderful, treasured memories even if they are accompanied by spreading arthritis in back, knees, and feet from injuries acquired in my escapades.

Two old companions are curled near me, enjoying the warmth. We celebrated Sunny the cat's twentieth birthday in early August. All but the first four weeks of his life have been spent in this house. He's very healthy for his age, but sometimes can't find his litter box and soils the rug beside it. It's his home too, so I just buy cheap rugs, keep the Febreze company in the profit column, and exchange irreclaimable throw rugs for new ones periodically.

His buddy Nikki is curled at his back. An AKC champion Papillon and the mother of two other champions playing in the yard, Nikki celebrated her 14th birthday over the summer. Now retired from show and motherhood, she's happy to spend her days in front of the fire, dreaming peacefully of past glories and plotting her next attempt to get the cat's food. She was diagnosed with Addison's disease three years ago, but happily medication and a carefully controlled diet have held it in check. A bout with pancreatitis four months ago has necessitated an even stricter diet which does not include the Savory Salmon by Fancy Feast that Sunny favors. I'm vigilant but not always fast enough to prevent her sneaky end runs to clean up the scraps left by her picky eater cat-pal.

The two have always been buddies. When Nikki went away on the show circuit, Sunny kept me busy opening closet doors for his inspection of hidden spaces looking for her. When Nikki returned with a CH in front of her name, he shadowed her everywhere and was only happy to sleep if he could cuddle near her. When she had puppies, he undertook the role of puppy sitter. The first time I found Sunny in the play pen, curled around a litter of three day old puppies while Nikki was enjoying a break in the yard, my heart missed a few beats. I was certain he'd decided the five-ounce squirming things were fresh meat. But no! The two helpless puppies, eyes and ears still sealed shut, were lying on his inside back leg with his tail curled around them, warm and snug in the care of their sitter. The puppies' adventures into eating solid food had to be supervised by their golden haired sitter, even if the offerings didn't come close to his epicurean taste for Savory Salmon.

Now both old friends are happy to snooze with me in front of the fire. The puppies the two raised together frolic and tumble outside in a yard dressed in the rainbow hues of late fall. Two of Nikki's puppies are AKC champions, one a veteran of Westminster Kennel Club show and *Animal Planet* experience. Nikki's granddaughter keeps in shape for her next show appearance by tearing around the yard outside with a bright orange leaf in her mouth, two body lengths ahead of her cousin. A bright red maple leaf is stuck to a plume tail streaming behind her pursuer, red against white, the colors of the Swiss flag. I don't think either have neutrality on their minds, however.

I laugh at their antics and their energy. But I am content to be inside, to relax and dream in front of the fire, to plan my next story or consider yet another sub-plot for my next book, to savor the list of books I want to read. Surrounded by companions, old and young, that are my family and my joy, life is comfortable, full of warm and wonderful memories of the past and happy expectations for the future.

Jean C. Keating photo

Autumn

The clang of the metal gate at the front of the shelter signaled the end of a busy Saturday marked by heavy traffic of visitors viewing the dogs and cats available for adoption. The old dog in the end enclosure gave an loud sigh as he settled his grey muzzle on his front paws and relaxed. It drew an instant expression of concern from the young dog in the enclosure next to his.

"Are you all right, Caden?" Sparkle's soft question was low and filled with worry. Caden couldn't see his friend for the six foot high wall of concrete blocks that separated their pens, but wire opening from the top of the blocks to the ceiling made communication possible.

"Just tired, Sparkle, don't fret about me!" the old dog responded.

"But I do worry," came the soft response from over the wall. "You didn't even try to attract that cute little boy who came to look at you. You've got to try to find a new home, Caden. You just have to try."

The old dog twisted a bit attempting to get more comfortable on the thin mat. "I'm not interested. I'm too old to train another boy. I just want to go to sleep and not wake up."

"Oh, Caden. You can't think like that. I know you're sad the boy is gone but it can't be helped. You must try to find another home, another boy to love."

Caden wisely changed the subject. "How about you? Did you find a likely prospect for a new home today? You were wagging all over, licking the hand of that little girl with the long curls."

"Oh, she was ever so nice. And her parents seemed to like me too, but they left without taking me. Do you think they might come back? I tried so hard to make them understand that I would make a good friend. I

21

wouldn't mind at all if she dressed me in doll clothes." The sadness and the poignancy in the soft voice came clearly over the wall. "I don't want to make a mistake again. But I don't know what I did wrong with my other family They seemed to love me. And be happy with me. But then the baby came and I thought we'd all be happy playing together. But then they didn't want me anymore. And they brought me here. I wish someone would tell me what I did wrong. I never meant to be bad."

Caden lifted his aging head from his paws, his voice sterner and sharper than he intended. "I've told you and told you, Sparkle, you didn't do anything wrong. Your previous family was inconsiderate, unfeeling, and totally selfish. They used you as a surrogate for a human baby and then when a human baby arrived threw you away without caring, without feeling. They're unworthy of your thoughts about them. You're lucky to be rid of them."

Sparkle's voice contained a bit of a sniffle. "Oh, I hope you're right. I will try awfully hard tomorrow to attract a new family but I hope the little girl comes back. It would be so nice to have a friend. But I worry about you Caden."

"Don't. Now let's get some sleep. Tomorrow is likely to be another busy day."

With another sniffle, Caden's little friend seemed to settle for the evening and the old dog returned to his musing.

The deepening Virginia twilight brought the smell of burning leaves. Caden's memory focused on a fall when he was a pup and Boy was an energetic scamp of ten or so. PawPa and Boy had worked together to rake the piles of bronze, red, orange, and yellow leaves into a huge pile. Caden had decided to contribute his help by jumping into the middle of the pile. A large oak leaf that had spent too much time snuggling up with a spider web had stuck to his face and covered one eye. In his hyperactive maneuvers to rid himself of the leaf, Caden had knocked Boy off his feet and into the pile of leaves with him. When PawPa came to help, boy and dog had managed to topple the man into the pile as well and they rolled around laughing at themselves till the

leaves were scattered over a wide area of the previously cleared yard. MeeMa came out to see what was causing the frivolity.

"Since you three can't be trusted to get a simple job of raking done," she chortled at them, "I suppose you'd best leave it till tomorrow. Come inside and I'll get you some hot chocolate to go with the warm brownies I've just taken out of the oven." She looked at Caden with a big smile, "But for you, young man, no chocolate. You'll have to settle for some butterscotch cookies."

Another sigh escaped the old dog. He missed his family, his Boy, PawPa, MeeMa. The staff and volunteers tried to make him comfortable, but a wooden platform over concrete and a thin mat were no replacement for the couch in front of the fire at his old home. And there was no replacement for the love of family.

Caden shifted his hips slightly, trying to get comfortable on the thinly padded wooden pallet. The twinge of arthritis in his left rear reminded him of the passing years, and his musing took him back to a time when life was good and he romped in the yard with Boy, chasing a foam football that PawPa had thrown in his direction. Boy tried to get it and the two of them rolled and frolicked in the sunshine.

But the years flew by as they often do, and Boy grew to a tall, determined young man. Caden remembered the night Boy had pulled him against his chest on the sofa and told him he had to go away, to a far away place where there were no autumn leaves, only sand. MeeMa and PawPa looked sad too, and MeeMa tried hard not to cry. They shared their usual comfort food, and the next day Boy was gone.

There were long evenings by the fire, and plenty of affection and attention from MeeMa and Pawpa. Caden and PawPa tried to play a little ball sometimes, but it wasn't the same. The bright spots were when letters would come from Boy and the three of them would sit on the sofa and read them over and over. The letters smelled of strange places, of sand and fear and smoke, but they smelled of Boy and so were precious to Caden.

Then one day, two fancy dressed soldiers came to the door, and their soft voices and sad countenances made MeeMa cry. PawPa thanked them as he drew MeeMa against his chest and guided her to the sofa where they hugged each other and cried. Caden pushed in between them, not understanding then that there would be no more letters from Boy, that he had fallen in that land far away called Afghanistan.

Life was never happy again. MeeMa didn't bake anymore, forgot things, sometimes didn't seem to even know who Caden was. PawPa tried hard to keep her spirits up, but one night the stress became too much, and PawPa didn't wake up anymore. Strangers came and took him away. Then they came and carried MeeMa to something they called a nursing home. There was no place for Caden. So they brought him here, to this shelter.

The old dog sighed again and drifted into a deeper sleep, one that masked for a time the discomfort of old age and loss of love and home. He awakened to a happy call from his neighbor.

"Caden, oh Caden. Wake up and come see," Sparkle called, a laughing note in her voice. "My little girl is back. Oh, she's back. Come see."

Caden slowly moved his stiff muscles and walked out into the outside area in time to see his beautiful neighbor wagging every inch of her shiny black body at the three humans that awaited her. A little girl of six or so with long blond curls reached eager hands to caress the excited little dog. Caden heard the man speaking to the volunteer as a bright red collar and leash were affixed to Sparkle's neck, "We've decided these two little ladies are a perfect match for each other, and we'd like to adopt her today and take her home."

There was no time for a long greeting between Sparkle and Caden, but he woofed a good-bye and good luck to her as she proudly pranced away with her new family.

Caden settled gingerly in a patch of sunlight. The days would be lonelier without Sparkle next door. This day would be long without much chance of a relief from boredom unless by chance he acquired another neighbor in Sparkle's old run. Visitors were plenty, but they rarely came down as far as Sparkle's empty pen and Caden's.

It was late in the afternoon and the sun was slipping low, when Caden heard someone call his name. He raised his head to view the stranger who appeared outside the gate to his pen.

"Hello, Caden. It's good to see you boy. You have no idea how difficult it's been to find you." The stranger's voice was unfamiliar but warm and caring. Caden sniffed but the man's scent was as unfamiliar as the voice. Slowly rising so that he didn't hurt his arthritic hip, Caden walked stiffly to the gate and put his muzzle near enough for the outstretched hand to rub his ears.

"I'm so sorry it took me this long to find you," the stranger said. "I'm Zack. Your Boy was my partner and buddy. You and his parents were all he talked about. I didn't have a family but he shared his with me. I promised him if anything happened to him, I'd find the three of you and bring you his love. "

Zack slapped the bottom of his left leg, which made a hollow sound as hand met plastic and metal of a false leg. "This wound slowed me down a bit, so by the time I got out of the hospital and rehab, your family was gone and I had a devil of a time tracing you. But I've found you now."

Caden was slowly taking in all that Zack was saying. This was Boy's friend. Now that his old brain could work more clearly, he seemed to detect a faint trace of a scent that had sometimes been present on Boy's letters. Boy's friend. Zack. And he was here.

A volunteer came up beside Zack. "Well, is this the dog you're looking for?"

"Yes. He sure is." Zack's voice was strong and comforting. "Now just what do I have to do to get this fellow out of here and home?"

Home? Caden's tail moved slowly for the first time in weeks. Could this be true? Did this stranger actually intend to take him to a new home? He'd not intended to try to make friends with another Boy. But perhaps this one wouldn't be too bad. He'd known Boy. They shared a love and memories. Maybe, just maybe, he could start again.

He wondered, as the gate to his enclosure was unlocked and a bright green collar and leash were affixed to his neck, if Zack knew how to bake butterscotch cookies.

Barbara Ball photo.

Brodie, An Alaskan Search and Rescue Star

The slender figure standing on the stage at this last event of the Bouchercon Mystery Convention in Anchorage held a microphone in one hand and the end of a blue dog leash in the other. Her red regulation shirt with the circular gold logo on the left matched the red service dog blanket adorning the alert golden, long-haired dog at her side.

Deb Gillis looked a bit ill at ease at the sheer numbers of people who flowed into the conference room and quickly filled the seats to capacity. The belt of equipment around her waist and dangling from her back pack seemed more than adequate to deal with anything that might arise. Brodie, the seven year old Nova Scotia Duck Trolling Retriever by her side, took one look at all the humans gathering in front of the podium and went into her clown act, rolling over on her back, kicking her four feet around in the air, and yowling. Brodie was delighted with the way her ice-breaking act softened up the crowd, and she kept it up through most of her human's presentation which followed.

Deb's presentation—more down home chat than dry talk—shared with her eager audience the training and organization of Alaska's Search and Rescue Dogs (ASARD). This all-volunteer group handles much of the search efforts for people, alive and dead, and for weapons in this wild and often physically challenging area of our nation. The only problems this group doesn't handle are the tracing and apprehension of criminals who may be armed; that is left to trained, professional police canines and their partners. Because this is a volunteer organization, each ASARD is owned and trained by the person who handles the dog; as such, each dog is likely to be trained in a slightly different way which corresponds to the dog's personal traits and responses to situations.

Brodie, Deb explained, likes to come back to her and jump up in front of her, lightly touching her front paws to Deb's knees as a signal of success in a task, and then rushing off again. So that is what is rewarded as a signal

of a successful find for Brodie. It might be slightly different for another dog because each is a unique personality.

The use of dogs is extremely effective and these talented canines and their dedicated owners are always in demand. Deb shared with us one situation in which dogs were not used which resulted in a humorous incident that was probably not funny to the people involved at the time. A hunter was thought to be missing in the cold and snow of early winter. Dogs were not used. The human rescuers searched frantically for the missing hunter without the help of these dedicated, four-legged, scent-talented searchers. Meanwhile, the hunter who was the object of the hunt was so embarrassed that he'd gotten himself lost in the first place, that he joined the rescue group and participated with them in the search for himself. He kept this up for many hours before finally admitting who he was. Had dogs been along, he would never have gotten away with that bit of chicanery.

Brodie thought this story was funny enough to go into another act of rolling on her back, waving her four legs in the air, and chortling, bringing even louder laughter from Deb's enthusiastic audience.

Deb smiled at her partner who continually up-staged her, then pulled a collar with a two-inch bell attached from her pack. Instantly Brodie was all professional and on the alert, looking expectantly at her human for a command, her fluffy tail waving her excitement and eagerness to comply.

"Because dogs such as Brodie will be working in heavy brush and woods, it is important that the individual they are seeking not mistake the approach of a rescue dog for a wild animal and either hide or shoot the rescuer, so Brodie wears this bell when she working."

She went on to explain that the bell's sound would not help the rescue party since the dog would be too far away for it to be heard, but the sound of its clapper as she moved would identify her as help rather than a threat.

Other than devious and embarrassed hunters, the hardest search quarries to deal with are children between the ages of five and eight; they are old enough for training to avoid strangers to have been assimilated but too young to understand they need to respond to rescuers.

Deb laughingly admitted that not all searches end the way they are depicted in movie and television presentations. She shared with the audience one situation in which she and Brodie were searching for a man who'd been missing for a considerable time in heavy snows. Brodie alerted by a stream bed and human rescuers combed the banks and shallows of very cold waters but recovered only some very smooth dental remains. Later lab work would prove these remains to be fragments of human cremation probably scattered in the stream for burial. They never did find the man.

The audience was filled with mystery writers. From the note taking going on, it was obvious that most had not realized that dental crowns survived nearly intact with cremation and would show up as a possible clue when human ashes were scattered.

Brodie remained alertly focused on her human and that bell in her hand, evidencing not one bit of embarrassment over this story.

When asked how she chose the puppy which she'd spent two years training and another year getting qualified as an Alaskan Search and Rescue Dog, Deb said she relied on a knowledgeable breeder. But then she shared with us one little story of how Brodie came to be chosen.

A rescue dog needs to be persistent and never give up when the going gets tough. The breeder would sprinkle tiny bits of bacon in a shag rug in her great room and turn the litter loose to find the bacon. Two of Brodie's litter kept after the bacon long after their siblings quit. Later one those two, Brodie, tracked her breeder all the way from the house to the barn when she wanted food and it was slow in being provided. And that's how Brodie got chosen to become Deb's dog and go on to become a valued search and rescue canine.

In the year to come, I wonder how many versions of Brodie's story will appear in books being written by the many mystery authors who cheered her this day!

Jean C. Keating photo

Dopey Was Anything But!

I named him Dopey! Our association began when he was an immature squirrel that seemed to enjoy teasing my pack of eight Papillons. He had my schedule memorized and was always sitting on the floor of the deck, flicking his bushy tail when I opened the door to let the dogs out in their yard for an outing. He wasn't deaf. He proved that many times when he arrived at the bird feeder before I could get there with seeds and treats.

He had to know the precursory sounds of the door being opened and the happy barking of a pack of excited little furballs from inside the house. But he'd wait until the first dog was through the door and almost close enough to step on that bushy little tail before taking off down the steps into the yard and racing for the nearest tree. Papillons are descendants of dwarf continental spaniels and proud of their principal duties as companions and couch potatoes, but they have not forgotten their ancestral love of the chase.

Dopey would make it to the nearest dogwood tree and scramble up the slender trunk just ahead of the pack of happily yipping toy terrors. Somehow I could never avoid adding to the din by screaming at the dogs to stop. Not that any of the four-footers ever paid the slightest attention to me!

As eight excited dogs tumbled over one another around the trunk of the dogwood, Dopey would scamper up the branches, leap to the larger tulip poplar beside it, and cross to the other side. The alpha female of the dog pack was usually the first one to note that Dopey had continued his trail to the ground on the other side of the larger tree and was headed for a small hole beneath the fence at the edge of the yard. He would manage to wiggle under the fence just ahead of eight dogs running at top speed after him. He would climb another tree just outside the yard to stop and chatter—probably in squirrel laughter—as the eight small bodies impacted with the chain length fence and each other, their momentum causing an amusing but thankfully non-harmful pileup at the fence.

Dopey could have chosen any number of trees after the tulip poplar as a safe haven; he could have stayed in the tree-tops and been safely out of reach of the small, five-to-seven pound dogs. But he seemed to love the chase as much as the dogs.

I worried that as he grew the small hole beneath the fence would be too small for his growing body and the dogs would smash into him before he could get away. I worried what the dogs would do if they actually caught the silly little squirrel. But as the days of summer turned into weeks and then months, I came to realize that Dopey would have calculated all of the aspects of his game too well to be caught.

I took to adding treats to the bird feeders for him. And then to placing a larger container on the rail of the deck with treats that he seemed to especially enjoy. Unshelled peanuts were his top favorite; sunflower seeds his second.

Toward the end of summer, I noticed that the game had changed. Dopey still led the dogs a merry chase across the yard, but now he sprinted up a tree closer to the fence's edge and stopped aiming for that tiny hole under the fence. When I'd observe him sitting on the edge of the deck waiting for the morning game, I marveled that the frail little body had turned into a fat, happy and mature squirrel.

By the next season, he was too busy or old to play, and the dogs missed him terribly. He still comes to his special feeder, enjoying his tributes and scolding sharply if I've forgotten to include his unshelled peanuts. The dogs and I hope that someday he'll father another little tease like himself. Meanwhile he has me busy insuring that his favorite treats are available at all times. I guess you would have to say he is anything but dopey!

Linda Lightfoot photo.

Jean C. Keating

First Manassas: An End to Innocence

On July 21, 2011, Virginia's governor, government officials, the head of the National Park Service, the entire service community of Prince William County, and special guests gathered on the hallowed grounds of the Manassas Battlefield Park near the slow-running waters of a wandering stream called Bull Run. They came to honor the men who fought and died there 150 years ago, to pay tribute to the courage, stubbornness, fortitude and dedication of those soldiers, Union and Confederate, whose blood saturated the ground beneath their feet. That day marked the end of innocence for both sides in a conflict that spanned four years of bloody war and claimed the lives of 620,000 men and 1.2 million horses.

Park Rangers volunteered from facilities all over Virginia to guide participants and guests on the hot July day. One of the speakers commented that 150 years ago the day had been hot, also, but not as hot as this day. Trooper Eric Evans from the Washington Capital Mounted Police stood prominently in front of the speakers' stand, providing sign language support to the crowd. Despite the 107 degree temperature, Evans managed to remain poised and neat in riding pants, highly polished boots and spurs, though he admitted that his horse, Stoney, was just as glad to have been left in a cool stall in Washington.

Speakers attempted to bring meaning to the horrific battle which opened the worst carnage ever experienced by our country.

Decades of controversy finally erupted in the battle fought on these rolling hills of open farmland on July 21, 1861. Sectionalism had increasingly divided the country. The extension of the railroads through the west linked western and northern segments of the country, forming a voting block that overpowered the south. One of the main quarrels was the tariffs—taxes—levied on goods from and to foreign countries. Higher taxes were imposed on Southern goods than on Northern ones, so southern profits were being sacrificed to support inferior northern products, in the minds of southerners.

Ethical and human rights issues of slavery fanned the divisiveness. John Brown's raid and his stated intent to cause insurrection and a blood bath in slave owning territories inflamed the south. Segments of the north, especially the radical elements of the abolitionist movement, intensified the ill feelings by treating Brown as a martyr and memorializing the day of his execution . Southerners saw the threats as hypocritical since it was northern interests that, at high profits, had brought slaves to American shores and sold them to southern agricultural enterprises, and then threatened secession from the Union in the early part of the 19th century when the importation of slaves was abolished. Southern attitudes solidified regarding the states' rights to decide on issues of slavery and on their choice of remaining a part of what was viewed increasingly as an unfair union. The Corwin Amendment passed by the United States Congress on March 2, 1861 would have forbidden attempts to subsequently amend the Constitution to empower the Congress to abolish or interfere with the domestic institutions of the states, but by that time, it was too little, too late. Sectionalism had replaced any willingness to talk or compromise.

Young men rushed to battle eager to 'save the Union' or 'preserve our state from invaders.' The Union called for enlistments for three months to put down the insurrection. The Confederacy saw this as a second revolution, and strongly held to their right to separate themselves from a government that took advantage of them as had the English crown.

The lines were drawn. Some 22,000 Confederate troops were poised at a sleepy little crossing of the Orange and Alexandria Railroads some 28 miles southwest of Washington. President Abraham Lincoln wanted the threat removed, concerned that the three month enlistments were drawing to a close, and rejected Union commander, General Irvin McDowell's concern that his 35,000 troops were green and not ready for combat. "You are green, it is true, but they are green also," he reassured McDowell. "You are all green alike."

Union politicians pressed for the suppression of the rebels. And so the blood bath began.

In their innocence, both sides expected a quick and easy victory. They were both wrong!

The forerunners of modern warfare and the medical support we use today for our wounded warriors in Iraq and Afghanistan had their birth here at First Manassas.

McDowell marched his green troops toward the Washington side of a stone bridge over Bull Run creek, making diversionary attacks there while he moved his main column of 20,000 north to flank the Confederate left. The first use of signal flags in battle came with the message from Porter Alexander to Colonel Nathan Evans: "Look out for your left, you are turned."

Evans shifted his reduced brigade of 1,100 men to meet the threat. They were soon reinforced by two of the four brigades, those under Brig. General Barnard Bee and Col. Francis S. Bartow, that had been rushed by railroad from the Shenandoah, the first tactical usage of railroads in battle. Even with these reinforcements, the badly outnumbered Confederate lines along Mathews Hill were forced to retreat and fall back toward Confederate lines a mile away on Henry House Hill.

The retreat became a rout and Union troops were jubilant, believing the 'only' battle of the war to be a crushing victory. McDowell rode along his lines proclaiming the win—a bit prematurely.

Union Captain James Ricketts sent his six 10-pound rifled cannon along the western slope of Henry Hill, chasing the fleeing Confederates. He ended up dueling with Confederate artillery 300 yards away. Inside the Henry house, 85-year-old Judith Henry lay bedridden and nearly blind, unable to escape the confusion and destruction of the heaviest part of the battle. Unlike the intentional aggression of Generals Sherman and Sheridan in later years of the war to attack and injure civilians supporting the Confederacy, Ricketts actions were motivated by his mistaken belief that the heavy fire he was taking originated from the Henry House. Ricketts trained his fire on the house mortally wounding the elderly woman who was the only civilian to perish in this first battle.

The First Brigade from the Confederate Army of the Shenandoah was deployed a mile in front of Mathews Hill, along the eastern slope of Henry Hill. Thirteen Confederate guns, sections of four batteries, unlimbered on the high ground, commanded by Brig. General T.J. Jackson, an artillery professor from Virginia Military Institute. When fired, the recoil from the guns threw them below the lip of the hill and rendered them safe from opposing Union forces as they were reloaded.

Union Captain Charles Griffin repositioned his howitzer section, two 12 pounders of his West Point Battery, to hurl artillery fire down the length of Jackson's lines. The similarity of battle flags and the more than 200 patterns of uniforms worn during this battle caused great confusion amid the smoke of musket and cannon fire. When the 33rd Virginia charged Griffin's howitzers, he failed to fire on them, mistaking them for Union troops. That one set of guns changed hands six times during the battle.

Captain John Imboden's Staunton artillery with four six-pounder smoothbore cannons were deployed on the descending slope just beyond the Henry house. His covering fire allowed the remnants of Bee, Bartow, and Evan's commands to regroup. Bee's last order to his men before being mortally wounded would bring the most well known and beloved title in the Confederate lexicon into being. "There stands Jackson like a stonewall. Rally behind the Virginians." A few hours later, Jackson's command to the 4th Virginia Infantry to "yell like furies" during a charge would introduce, for the first time, the eerie sounds of the Rebel yell.

Spectators, politicians and socialites from Washington city added to the confusion and congestion as Union forces attempted an orderly retreat. When the Stone Bridge over Bull Run became clogged with overturned carriages and debris from shelling by Confederate artillery, the retreat turned into a rout called the "Great Skedaddle". A brief belief that Confederate independence was assured was quickly dispelled by reality as most of the three-month Union volunteers began to reenlist for three years.

Confederate medical services were strained beyond their resources, as they struggled to deal with their 1,580 wounded as well as the critically wounded Union soldiers left behind. Their existing procedure of having a surgeon and an assistant surgeon assigned to each regiment did not work, and sweeping transitions to front line hospitals with swift transport of wounded to hospital pavilions was employed by both Union and Confederate forces as the war progressed. Two miles behind the battlefield park, a lasting memorial to the frantic attempts at care of the wounded is preserved at the Ben Lomond plantation which was a Confederate field hospital during First Manassas. The bloody operating room shared space with an officer's portable desk and a chair about which is draped the coat of a 2nd Lt. Isaiah Tanner, pulled from the line with the 1st Virginia Cavalry to assume duties as surgeon because his previous medical experience was needed more here at Ben

Lomond. Today, the concept of various levels of care, from MASH units at the front and quick transport to back line division hospitals is still the means of caring for our current wounded warriors.

After First Manassas, Confederate authorities would quickly move to replace the first national flag with a more easily discernible battle flag. The more well known Cross of St. Andrews would come into being.

Despite the confusion of uniforms, battle flags, poor discipline, and lack of training, the bravery, dedication, stubbornness, and self-sacrifice that is an enduring symbol of these men, Confederate and Union, leaves visitors to this hallowed site with a deep reverence for those who clashed here.

The tributes to these men and to the history they left us were supported by 8,200 re-enactors who assembled from 21 states and two foreign countries to recreate the battle and keep alive the knowledge of their history, the challenges they faced, and the fortitude with which they addressed those challenges. They shared their tributes with the more than 12,000 spectators who came to view their efforts.

Just getting around with that many reenactors was a challenge. Brendon Hanafin, Chief of Historical Preservation for Prince William County, finally got through into Pageland Farm where the re-enactment of the battle was held, but it took almost thirty minutes to go the short half mile.

During that time Hanafin entertained this reporter and two photographers with a story about one unforeseen problem caused by the extremely hot conditions. A large silver tanker truck of water had been moved on site for the 480 horses taking part in the reenactment. However, sitting in the sun caused the water to heat up, the horses wouldn't drink hot water, so an emergency run for ice—for the horses—had to be worked into the many other plans necessary to accommodate humans, mules,

 cannons, re-enactors, spectators, a line of 12 ambulances on the scene for emergencies, and a large tent of modern medical personnel to cover heat-related and other problems.

One young re-enactor interviewed earlier didn't make it to Manassas. John David Mayo had begun re-enacting at 16, and for 11 years had enjoyed being a part of celebrating this link to the past. His situation is unusual in that a heart condition has made the highly demanding physical activity a challenge.

In spite of Mayo's health problems, four different groups demonstrated the consideration of these 'brothers in arms' by their willingness to have him join their groups. Asked how he could possibly carry the 12 pound replica of a civil war rifle with his heart problem, J.D. smiled and admitted that the units all proposed he serve as the fifer, responsible for carrying only his tiny fife and a haversack.

But all re-enactors must be dressed in appropriate

period dress—which usually means a wool outfit. Asked how he managed to run across open fields in a wool costume, J.D. grinned and replied, "I'm always an early casualty." Given the extreme heat of this particular reenactment, J.D. wisely decided to stay home.

In the Confederate artillery encampment, Collins Bret rested in the oppressive heat beside an antique table which he brought from Kansas City, Missouri along with tin plates and antique bottles revived with labels which are authentic reproductions. The cannon which he and his crew of 12 brought to this re-enactment was one of 47 on the Confederate side.

Rob Glazer, a member of the James City Cavalry Camp, Sons of Confederate Veterans, was participating at Manassas as a member of the 5th Virginia. He explained that organizers make certain that participants conform to authentic gear and uniforms for whatever battle they are portraying, that the units are run like a regular army unit, drills and practice are required before each re-enactment, and if you don't drill, you don't participate.

Re-enactors pay for their own uniforms and gear, about $1,500- $1,800 for an infantry unit, pay to belong to the organization, and pay an enrollment fee for each re-enactment in which they participate. Pity the poor artillery re-enactors who must drag along the cannon, the limber, the gear to load, and the horses in addition to their tents and personal gear.

Through it all, these devotees maintain a strict adherence to history. Although the uniforms noted in one photo resemble those of several other Union units, the flag identifies them as Confederate. Imagine trying to determine if this was the first National flag of the Confederacy or the Union flag in the haze and smoke. One hundred and fifty years ago and at this re-enactment

of First Manassas, not a single flag displaying the Cross of St Andrew was in sight. It hadn't been created in July of 1861.

This only battle was but the beginning of four years of war. But these combatants stayed, toe to toe, understanding now the resolve and determination of their opponents, but fighting and dying for what each believed was right and just, no longer innocent.

Ira Abbott and Beverly Abbott photos

Gifts of Love

Linda Fairchild tried with little success to get a sip of coffee from the mug she held unsteadily in her hand. The determined Papillon who occupied her lap butted her black head and ears under Linda's hand demanding a continuing head and ear rub. Although the little canine weighed in at only seven plus pounds, her determination to have the visiting human's attention was sufficient to render coffee consumption difficult.

"Twinkle, you brat, will you let me get at least one sip of my coffee, before I continue with providing worship to your person," Linda chuckled.

"I'm sorry. I'll make her get down if you want," Genna Colt responded, though the trace of laughter in her voice betrayed her amusement at the little dog's antics.

"Oh, no. She's no problem. I'm just enjoying and marveling at the remarkable changes in her. When she came from Papillon Rescue she was terribly afraid of people. Except for her fat belly due to her pregnancy, she was painfully thin and her coat was dry, coarse, and sparse. However have you changed that fearful scarecrow into this beautiful assured little butterfly?"

"Hah! My secret weapon!" Genna smirked. "Well, as you probably remember, Sky and my other dogs often go to my friend Barbara Bennett at Foxwood Grooming. At first I was reluctant to send Twinkle because she was so fearful of new places and people, but finally I tried sending her to Barbara for grooming. Barb is so gentle and caring, and she took extra time with little Twinkle. After about three visits, Twinkle began to look forward to the new sights and sounds, the other little dogs, and began to really come out of her fear reaction to new stuff."

Linda finally managed a sip of coffee in spite of the tiny head that still pushed under her hand demanding attention.

"Twinkle's coat is soft, shining, and beautifully abundant. Is that Barb's doing also?"

"Oh, yes. She uses something with magical oil in the conditioner that keeps all my dogs in fine coat."

"Wow. Maybe I should take Freddie to her. I can't seem to keep his ear fringes from breaking off."

Genna chuckled. "Well, unfortunately you'll have to travel a good distance now, since Barb is moving to Voorheesville, New York, and opening another Foxwood Groomers there."

"Drats!" Linda grimaced. "Why am I always finding out about great things too late!" Not expecting an answer to her rhetorical question, she continued. "When are you planning to send Twinkle to her forever home?"

"I'm not. I'm keeping her."

Linda's knowing grin accompanied her abandonment of her coffee mug. She sat the now empty mug on the coffee table in front of her and applied both hands to rubbing and head patting the eager dog reclined half way in her lap. Linda's immediate reaction to Genna's statement was to wonder how the two chief males in her friend's life would react to such an event. Genna's writer husband Jonathan would probably take it in stride but her Velcro boss dog Sky would most likely balk at any competition for Genna's attention.

"Oh, really. And just how do Jonathan and Sky react to that? For that matter, what does Papillon rescue think of that? You know the purpose of providing foster care is to retrain, rehabilitate, find forever homes, and place needy dogs in them. You're not supposed to keep them. You're supposed to settle them elsewhere and make room for another rescue."

Genna ducked her head and shrugged her shoulders, giving physical evidence that she understood her friend's comments. But the stubborn chin lifted in determination and she responded, "I don't care. Twinkle stays here. I've been a helpful foster home in the past. My first foster was named Twinkle also."

Genna settled deeper into her chair as her mind drifted back twelve years to the first time she offered her home and love to a rescue in need of care. That Twinkle came from a puppy mill. She passed through many hands who attempted to help. Competent vet care removed her twisted uterus and infected teeth. In Genna's care, she'd learned to trust humans, and soon Genna found her a forever home with a loving and needy human. Twinkle (the First) never put her tail up or learned to climb stairs in her life. But she provided a reason to go on, a sense of family, and a source of love to a lonely woman who'd lost her husband and only child to a drunk driver. Together they picked up the pieces of their lives and became a stronger unit than the sum of two small and hurting parts. Two broken lives, not one, were mended.

Spring was another little butterfly with a sad past, without toys or a chance to learn to play. She passed through PCA rescue to Genna's foster care. Genna found her a forever home with a badly hurting human. Balancing the work for a doctoral degree while working full time is a huge challenge for anyone, much less a not-so-young single who lived alone except for a tiny dog. The sudden and unexpected death of her only companion, a five-year old Papillon, threw this gifted and determined lady into depression and a questioning of the worth of all the effort. Spring came to a house full of toys she didn't know how to use and a grieving human whose tears she quickly learned to dry. Renamed Bijou, little jewel, she soon made a place for herself, reestablished the twosome as a family unit, and re-warmed the spot beside the computer chair where her grieving new human studied and worked. Three years later Bijou wore her own tiny mortar board at her 'graduation' party where she was awarded her very own 'doggie doctorate' for helping her human achieve her dream. Today they are a devoted twosome at the beach, at home cooking and feeding the birds, and often in the office of a high school where Bijou has taken over the job of Assistant to the Principal. Their Christmas letters and annual picture to Genna made her cry with joy.

"I've done my job as foster mom in the past," Genna affirmed with conviction, "but this Twinkle stays here, forever. After all we've been through together, raising her two babies and seeing them safe to forever homes, I can't bear to part with her."

Linda reached across the coffee table to warmly fold one of Genna's hands in her own. "I'd expected nothing less after what the two of you had gone through. But tell me, what do Jonathan and Sky think about the permanent addition of another female to the family?"

Genna chuckled. "Jonathan just says, 'we'll make sure she continues to know she's loved.' Sky says she's not sharing the bed in the master bedroom."

Jean C. Keating photo

It All Depends on the Cat

"How do Papillons get along with cats?"

The question is raised by 80% of all prospective pet buyers of Papillons. With all my years of living with these bright, active little dogs I've never decided on an exact answer for the question. Except with another question. Or a stalling technique like, "It depends on the cat."

They get along fine with MY cats. But then there's that question, "Are the two soft walking, purring and meowing inhabitants of my home really cats?"

In late 1989 I brought home tiny kittens, my first-ever felines, waifs that were crying out for help. A seminar in Fredericksburg ended early because of the pending arrival of Hurricane Hugo. Two little kittens didn't have mother or cover after the hotel did their hurricane-preparation stashing of outside furnishings and equipment. So I packed one yellow-and-white and one black-and-white ball of fluff along with my luggage and came home. My vet pronounced the waifs to be four-week old kittens, and put them on formula administered with a doll bottle. My two mature Papillon bitches supervised my efforts at feeding and clean-up, convinced I couldn't do it correctly on my own.

My first hint that cats might be a different worry from my normal puppy raising was the kittens' first-time climb up the side of the sofa. Such tame adventures were followed by more heart-stopping ones like falling off the back of sofas and walking along the second-floor balcony rail overlooking the first-floor living room.

Our second vet visit had the doctor and his assistant rolling on the floor laughing, mostly at me. By now the yellow-and-white male answered, if only in my  mind, to Sunny and the black-and-white female was distinguished in my conversations as Misty, although she rarely answered to anything. Both kept batting and scratching at the hands and fingers of vet and assistant. "No," I kept telling them. "Stop biting." My words were reinforced by slight taps on pink noses. All of which brought no improvement in behavior from my tiny felines and more amused chuckles from my vet.

"Have you ever owned a cat before?" my vet managed despite suppressed laughter.

"No," I admitted while attempting another correction to a tiny paw scratching at my hand.

"Well, maybe I'd better explain." The vet made a valiant attempt to wipe the grin off his face as he instructed, "Cats don't, you see, recognize anything like 'No' or 'Nada' or any instructions which require them doing other than what they want. They're not going to behave like your puppies. They don't care whether they please you or not."

"Well," says I, determined not to put up with what, to a confirmed dog lover, was unacceptable behavior, "don't tell them they're cats. We'll just tell them they're puppies."

Never missing a breath, my vet pulled the long fringe

49

in each ear of the nearest kitten upward and outward, gave me a mock serious look and replied, "Funniest Papillon I've ever seen."

From that defining moment on, I never looked back. I raised two fur balls with retractable claws to be twelve-pound and nineteen-pound long-legged, long-bodied, confident, and sometimes obedient companions. They came when called because each grew to understand I'd close the door and leave them in a deserted room. They played with the dogs because they like to play and the canines were always ready.

One young Papillon would chase Sunny, both of them tearing around living and dining room at Rusty's top speed.

My puppy training books didn't seem to cover the situation, however. Sunny never attempted to leap up on surfaces to get out of the way or run fast enough to outdistance the dog. When Rusty would tag the cat from the rear, the two would collapse into a heap and take a nap. Usually Sunny would regain his energy first, back up to the dog and pretend indifference while Rusty roused from his nap, grabbed a big hunk of cat fur on the cat's back and gave it a yank. Then the chase would be on again—with the cat chasing the dog.

Misty, the smaller, female cat was fastidious about cleaning herself, but Sunny, the male, proved to be a slob in his early years. His coat was matted and unkempt and my vet got more chuckles at my frequent vet visits with Sunny in attempts to determine illnesses that didn't exist. Sunny was just a slob of a teenager. I started grooming him like a Papillon. He liked the attention and the scratching, but objected strongly when the comb pulled on a mat. He was inclined to growl and snap his tail, all of which got him no sympathy and a few extra squirts of grooming spray. He knew better than to

bite me; he tried it once and I growled at him. When a few bites at the comb didn't stop my pulling out mats, he wisely resigned himself at two years of age to doing his own grooming. From then on he presented himself as a sleek, shiny golden tabby.

Papillons are talkers, and will whoo-whoo—a combination howl that goes into a bark and may end with a whine—to beg for treats. Sunny's purr was too soft to compete for attention, so he started coughing. The first few times he positioned himself in the middle of my desk and coughed, I suspected hair balls and prepared for the worst. He had to bat the can of cat treats off my desk's shelf and cough in my face before I got the hint. Thereafter nightly routines included the dogs whoo-whooing for treats and Sunny coughing to signal he wanted his share.

At three years of age he took up puppy-sitting. One of the Papillons had a singleton puppy, and Sunny watched in fascination from the top of the dining room table while Minnie busied herself with her motherly duties of feeding and cleaning her baby. By this time, I'd accepted him as just a funny sized dog myself, so didn't think anything about it. Then Minnie went outside for a little rest and relaxation from motherhood and left tiny, three-week old Urchin alone. When I glanced in the playpen a bit later, all I could see in the sleeping box was a very large, golden tabby stretched out with a smug look on his face. Between choking and trying to start my heart up again, I reached for Sunny. I thought he'd eaten the puppy. I was mentally kicking myself for being careless, cursing him for being a cat.

My grab for the cat was arrested by the appearance from beneath his upper back leg of two tiny front paws and a puppy's head. With heart still skipping beats and doing flips, I lifted the cat's top hind leg to find Urchin snugly lying on Sunny's inner thigh, enjoying the warmth of the big cat's body and long fur to keep herself comfortable during her mother's absence. The silly grin on Sunny's face announced his satisfaction with his self-appointed role. He continued it through years of litters to come.

Last year, I hosted a birthday party for my seventeen-year-old foundation bitch. Her descendants were invited to attend, accompanied by their humans. Many of the canines had not been home for eight years, having left as four-month-old puppies to go with their humans to their forever homes. All of the returning dogs entered the house proudly, greeted me warmly and then went looking for Sunny. The big yellow whatever came running downstairs and up to each grown dog with perfect assurance that he knew them, that they'd welcome him, and that the humans who returned as escorts were friendly.

According to my cat books, that simply isn't normal feline behavior. Misty was certainly nowhere to be found during this birthday party attended by thirty-one dogs and twenty-nine humans. So while I've lived with Papillons and with two cats, I haven't got a clue as to whether they'll get along with your cat.

Well, there's the phone again. And here's that same question.

"Ah! Well, it depends on the cat."

Jean C. Keating photos

Jamestown's 400th Birthday

"Yiiiiiikes!" Little Puff screamed. He enjoyed the faint scent of the shower gel that still clung to her skin, but the metal buttons on his mistress' pajama top were cold against his belly as she hugged him tightly against her. The buttons also jangled as they hit together and rang loudly in his big butterfly ears.

He whimpered softly and pulled away from his mistress.

"What's wrong, my brave little one?" his mistress queried.

Puff dropped his face to touch his nose against the higher of the two buttons, clanking the first one into the second one below it on the blue top.

"Are you still worrying about that metal chest plate on your costume for the parade?"

His mistress was tuned in at least. Puff was grateful for that. He didn't have her gift of speech. His communications were with eyes and body language. And he wanted so desperately to make her understand that he just couldn't do what she'd asked of him the day before.

He tried to snuggle closer to her, but those dratted cold metal buttons hit him in the stomach again. He shivered and pushed away from her tight embrace with his tiny paws against her shoulders.

His problem with cold metal had all started when he and his mistress had visited that little town down the road from his home in Williamsburg. It wasn't a town really, just a festival park and some buildings that were displays of what had been. His mistress had explained to him that it was a historical site where English settlers had landed 400 years ago to begin the settlement of America. Well, he didn't understand 400 years. And he wasn't certain whether she meant something she called 'dog years' or the passage between summer and summer. He was just glad that his little orange vest with the SERVICE DOG patch meant he could go with her through the park.

Then his mistress started talking with another human friend at that park and that friend explained with a worried tone in her voice that THE QUEEN had expressed concern that the birthday party wasn't giving enough credit to someone called Captain John Smith.

Puff wasn't sure who the two women meant by THE QUEEN. But he knew about birthday parties. His mistress gave him one every year. Puff didn't know that parks had birthday parties. He knew he didn't like to wear his birthday hats. He wondered how a park could have a birthday hat!

"I know," he heard his mistress say. "The Queen is coming for a parade down Duke of Gloucester Street, and we'll dress up in costumes to celebrate the festivities. Puff can come as Captain John Sniff in honor of the man who led the settlers and made the Jamestown settlement a success. "

It was only later that Puff came to learn what his mistress had in mind for him. When his costumer presented him with the outfit his mistress had ordered, it had a metal jacket. Cold, hard metal. Two solid pieces held around his body by leather laces. The shiny surface hurt his eyes, and the cold around his chest and back was very uncomfortable. But it was the noise that the two metal pieces made as they clanged together and pulled against the leather ties keeping the two pieces of metal together that really bothered his keen hearing and his big beautiful ears.

In spite of his intent to be a good dog and cooperate, he'd whined, and twirled and tried to avoid the metal covering. He dropped his tail and his ears were so low they stuck out each side of his head instead of being carried in their usual erect state like the wings of the butterfly for which his breed was named. He was terrified by the idea of having to wear the thing and ashamed at his uncooperative behavior.

The costumer and his mistress had gotten into a long and heated exchange of words.

"It has to be metal," the costumer had said. "All the pictures of John Smith, even his court dress, show him in a metal breast plate. Many of those pictures also show him in a metal helmet."

"Puff doesn't like it," his mistress replied.

"Well, you want him to be authentic, don't you? You said for me to design an authentic costume for him," the costumer replied huffily. "So he needs to wear a metal breast plate and a metal helmet."

"I think not," Puff's mistress said. "There has to be something else you can do. Puff doesn't like the metal pieces to this costume."

Puff wasn't certain why he needed to be AR-THIN-TICK. Were ticks going to be a part of this outfit? He certainly hoped not!

His mistress had taken the metal off him and they'd left the costumer's shop soon after. But the thought of that metal contraption had bothered him the rest of the day. And he'd carried the worry into his dreams. In his nightmares, metal clanked and ticks hid under the breast plate and bit him and he couldn't get at them through the metal.

Now the large metal buttons on his mistress' pajama top brought back all the horror of that costume.

His mistress seemed to understand his pain.

"Don't you worry about that costume, my little hero. You'll have something to wear as Captain John Sniff for the parade that will not bother you at all," she promised. "Now let's take this phone back upstairs where it belongs, find something for me to wear that won't bother you and see if we can get back to sleep for the rest of the night."

Back upstairs, his mistress replaced the cold metal buttons and the blue top with a soft pink shirt. She returned the cordless phone to its stand. Then she and Puff settled back into the big bed and he snuggled close against her pillow and tried not to think about metal pins or breast plates for the rest of the night.

Puff and his mistress were up late for breakfast after the excitement of the night before. Puff was feeling much better. He'd not been bothered by nightmares of clanking metal for the remainder of the night, and he was enjoying his Cheerios until his mistress remarked, "Hurry up and finish your breakfast, Puff, so we can go back and check on your new costume."

ARGH!!!! Visions of metal chest covers! Memories of clanking pieces of metal! Puff cringed. His large ears drooped and stuck out toward each side of his head. And his tail dragged the floor.

"Now, stop that," his mistress said. "I'm not going to ask you to put on anything else made of metal. I'm sure this latest version of your outfit as Captain John Sniff will be comfortable and perfect for you to wear."

Puff wasn't at all certain of that. But he finished the rest of his Cheerios and followed his mistress out the door and to the costumers' shop once more.

The costumer was all smiles as she brought out an outfit for Puff and his mistress to consider. Puff sniffed apprehensively then began to slowly wave his tail so that the long fringes fanned the table. The chest and back piece of this new costume as well as the hat were

made of soft, grey leather with raised areas to look like dents in metal. The only metal Puff could detect was in small silver buttons which circled the brim of the hat and accented the collar of the grey breast covering.

He stood happily as his mistress put the pants and then the breast covering and long sleeved shirt on him. His costume even had a sword. But the sword wasn't made of metal. It was made of paper and glue.

"You look so handsome, my dear one," said his mistress with a broad smile on her face. "Oh, thank you," she said to the costumer. "You have done a wonderful job for us, and he seems very pleased to wear it."

Puff wouldn't have gone so far as to say he was pleased. The rough white shirt was scratchy. The buff colored pants were even worse. They seemed to be made of sandpaper. But the rest of the costume was soft against his white coat. He could wear it without being too uncomfortable. More importantly, it was quiet. It didn't click and clang and make noises that hurt his ears. And he was glad that he could please his mistress.

When the Queen arrived to help celebrate the 400th anniversary of the founding of Jamestown, Puff waited along the parade route. He was dressed in his costume to honor Jamestown's founder, Captain John Smith, but it was made with a soft LEATHER breast covering. His mistress kept introducing him to the people standing beside them on Duke of Gloucester Street as Captain John Sniff. He licked hands presented to him and waved his tail in response to their greetings. He was getting a bit nervous, however. He didn't want to embarrass his mistress. He was worried what THE QUEEN would think of him. Everyone spoke of her with great reverence. He didn't know exactly who she was but decided she was right up there with FIRST DOG GOD. He hoped she wouldn't be too displeased with him.

When THE QUEEN finally drove by in a fine carriage with fancy uniformed attendants, she gave him a beautiful smile as she passed and waved at him.

"See!" he woofed happily at his mistress. "I may not be AW-THIN-TICK, but at least I don't clang when I walk."

Jean C. Keating photos.

Justice

Little Red glided up the porch steps with the grace and smoothness that always seems to be the hallmark of a cat's movement. At nine months, he'd almost caught up with his large paws and his sire's impressive size, but the plump mole he carried in his mouth slowed his motion this afternoon. He reached his objective, the feet of the woman dressed in a black turtleneck and jeans who stood just outside the door from the porch to the garage.

"And what do we have here, smart boy" the soft voice chuckled. "Your first mole? Or just the first I've seen you bring?" Jenny Cochran reached to stroke the big head of the young cat, fondling the deep red stripes against the white coat. "But the porch isn't the place for your prize."

Picking up a large plastic tweezers from among several

on the railing, she picked up the mole and continued in a steady voice. "Now come with me and I'll show you where your contribution goes." Backing through the door into the garage, she encouraged the young cat to follow her to a spot inside the garage, a black plastic bag spread between four bricks. There were already four other dead moles scattered around on the bag as well as one tiny field mouse. Dropping Little Red's contribution on the black plastic among the other bodies, she continued, "This is where you leave your contributions, see! And tonight we'll give them to Mr. and Mrs. Owl for their dinner."

Little Red followed her every movement, meowing steadily and rubbing around her ankle.

"Oh, you are spoiled, aren't you." Jenny picked him up with some difficulty, the tiny kitten of a few months ago having reached some fifteen pounds of healthy coat and muscle. She flipped him on his back to hold him like a human baby and his loud meows changed to a contented purr. "You are getting too big for Mommy to pick you up like this. My back won't allow this." Little Red purred even louder.

A tousled female head capped in auburn curls ducked into the garage through the side door, accompanied by a large black lab. The oval faces of the two and the beautiful copper hair easily identified them a sisters, though Jenny's eyes were a dusty brown with green lights, while her sister Connie Holland's eyes were big and blue, the color intensified by the denim jacket and pants she wore. Stormy, her black lab, calmly came to her left side and sat quietly ignoring Little Red who hissed and snarled but did not try to run away.

"You know you need to take more care with your back." Connie's words did little to convey anything but amusement, since she knew her sister well enough to realize her cautions would fall on deaf ears.

"I know, but he still enjoys his kitten expressions of affection." Seeing the blanket in her sister's hand for the first time, she continued, "What are you up to now?"

"Stormy has alerted to the intrusion of someone down the back road, so we're going out looking for whatever waif has been dumped this time." Connie's eyes flashed the anger both sisters always felt toward the selfish and unfeeling humans who dumped dogs and cats on their property, too callous and uncaring to worry over the animals' pain and loneliness at being abandoned. Many were underfed, often females pregnant through failure of their despicable humans in taking proper cautions to prevent problems in the first place.

"Do you want me to go with you?" Jenny asked.

"No. Just my trusty Search and Rescue canine will be enough," Connie responded, her eyes taking on the love and respect for the dog by her side and her left hand reached to stroke the sleek, black head. "Too many strange humans might frighten the poor animal into running deeper into the woods.

"Okay," responded Jenny. I'll make certain the quarantine room in the shed has fresh bedding, water and the food dish is washed. I'll put both dog and cat food outside for your easy reach as soon as you figure out what we're rescuing. If it's a bigger problem, call me. I'll make certain we have some hot gruel ready in case this in another situation of malnutrition. Do you want me to alert Dr. Frank?"

Connie shook her copper curls. "No, let the poor man rest until we know what we're dealing with." The sisters' vet was a saint who always threw himself 100% into helping with their many rescue efforts.

The sisters lived in a big, old, but well kept up, farm house set in the middle of six acres. Porches on the front and back of the house were covered and the wooden floors were softened by old rugs mostly for the comfort of animals who came to call. The garage was equipped with a large animal door which the seven outdoor cats used to come and go, many leaving their daily contributions of dead moles and mice on the expanse of black plastic. In winter, an electric heater kept the garage warm for any animal that needed a sleeping place.

Except for the acre surrounding the house, the rest of the property was left in dense, natural woods. Unfortunately, a bumpy road lead into the woods for access to the small lake on the property, and no amount of NO TRESPASSING signs or a locked gate at the beginning of the road had yet deterred determined humans from driving in and dumping unwanted animals down the road into the woods.

Connie waved and said, "Off on another rescue mission. Wish us luck!" Stormy moved out as though plastered to his mistress' left knee. Little Red finally relaxed again and focused his attention on the placement of his dead mole on the black plastic rectangle.

"Come on in the house. I'll bet you'd like a snack. Growing kittens always need more to eat."

The two passed quietly into the kitchen. Jenny was careful to keep her voice low and not to go too near the window. The back porch was crowded at this time of day with a beautiful buck and three female deer. It was hunting season, and Mr. Deer was safely settled on the rug on the back porch. He was a very smart deer, which is why his rack sported about six points. Jenny was never exactly sure how one counted points or just why anyone would want to kill such a magnificent animal. During hunting season he brought his small band of three does and rested on the rug on her back porch during the day. When night fell, and the hunters in back of her house went away, the little group went off to feed. Jenny never tried to feed them, except when the ground was covered in snow in the winter, leaving them wild and free but marveling at the intelligence that drew them to the protection of her porch.

The woods in back of the sister's property was posted, but it did not prevent hunters from coming on their property to request a waiver to hunt their woods. Her answer was an emphatic NO and a caution that they owned shotguns and knew how to use them against intruders who ignored NO TRESPASSING signs.

Mr. Deer alerted as Jenny passed by the kitchen window, but her softly spoken "It's just me. Go back to sleep..." was sufficient to reassure him that he was still safe.

She pulled a small snack of wet cat food with a  sprinkling of shredded cheese from the fridge and placed it in a small bowl, putting it on the floor for Little Red. The smell brought the huge grey king of the house from the other room. His magnificent coat of grey fur matched his beautiful green eyes, which at the moment was focused on the food in front of Little Red. "No, you do not need a snack," Jenny cautioned him with a chuckle. "You're going to get too fat to sleep on my bed if you keep eating every time one of the kittens does."

The boss cat of the house was nearing 19 pounds now, but had been brought to the house by one of the outdoor cats and left on the black plastic square in the garage with the dead moles. He'd fit into the palm of Jenny's hand at that point, but was a solid grey. Being a devoted Southern lady she'd named him Thomas

Jonathan Jackson Robert Edward Lee but called him Tommie Lee for short. The sounds from the second bedroom made it plain that the band of six five-week old kittens had picked up the scent of treats and wanted to join the party.

Little Red swiftly consumed the remainder of his treat and went to the outside door, requesting exit from the house. He was not interested in facing down Tommie Lee under any conditions and was less interested in playing with his younger siblings that were trying their best to get out of the bedroom.

Little Red's dam had recognized many months ago the sanctuary offered by the sisters' home and had one-by-one brought her brood of five kittens (including Little Red) to the friendly home in the woods. She and her kittens had been fed and cared for and given a corner nest in the garage. She had the freedom to come and go at will, but always the assurance of a safe place and plenty of food at all times. Unfortunately, a visit to Dr. Frank, with the intention of spaying her, showed she was already pregnant and too far along to risk spaying. When she delivered again, mother and six young kittens were confined to the house until she could be spayed. That had been safely done several weeks ago, but the younger kittens showed no signs of being interested in the outdoors. Arrangements with the local shelter had found a home for five of them together on a farm some miles away. One of the kittens had captured the sisters' hearts with her bossy ways and would remain as an indoor cat.

Some two hours later Connie and Stormy returned. Connie's facial expressions were a mix of smug satisfaction and anger. Wrapped in a blanket in her arms was a scared, starved and shivering little dog, a mixture of spaniel and Chihuahua. One ear flopped and one stood erect.

Two hours later, bathed, flea protected, and wrapped in a warm towel, the sisters had given the starving little waif a nourishing meal of soft food laced with Nutrical and bedded her down in the isolation room at the corner of the garage. A tiny clock tucked into her blanket assured her that she wasn't alone, although the occasional cat's head that peeked over the partition provided ample evidence that the little abandoned dog was a part of a family now.

As the sisters walked back to the kitchen for a start

on dinner, Stormy came in for a proper amount of praise for his quick find and consoling of the newest rescue. Jenny finally had time to ask, "I can understand your smug satisfaction when you arrived and your anger. I just wish we could put a stop to this dumping on our property of all these animals in need."

Connie responded, "I just did, at least I think I did."

"How?"

"Remember that large package that came last week. You asked what it was and I told you I'd tell you later?"

"Yes," Jenny responded, "but you never did tell me."

"Well, I ordered one of those tire ripping strips. You know the one law enforcement people throw across the highway to stop fleeing criminals?'

Jenny looked puzzled. "For what?"

"I put it out across our road just a bit past our gate which doesn't seem to ever stop these dumpers. And I covered it with leaves, so it isn't visible. It's just by the little turnout on the right, so we'll know to use the turnout and avoid the strip."

"Very funny, Little Sister. And just what do we do when the jerks walk up to the house and ask for help?

"Tell them to use their cell phones. We don't open our doors to strangers."

"Even funnier, Little Sister. You know that road is a dead zone. You can't get pickup on a cell down there."

Connie laughed. "I know! Ain't justice great. The jerks will have to walk the three miles back to the main road."

Linda Lightfoot cat photos, Bill Bryan dog photo.

My Little Orange Crabs
By Puff the Papillon

My frustrations started a few weeks ago, when a group of my human's friends got together and decided to put on this big dog show. It's called a National Specialty. I've never been to one, but my human tells me we're going next April.

Humans seem to pick little creatures to represent big events in their lives. They call them logos. Since these humans decided to hold this dog show in Maryland, they picked a little crab as their mascot. This had something to do with the state of Maryland being represented by a fat, blue edible with more legs than I have.

You know, of course, that humans don't have a very keen sense of hearing. Nor do they always pay close attention to what is being said in the present. It has something to do with being too worried about something they call Past and Future. Anyway, one of the humans mentioned that a certain delightful squeaky was available in the shape of a BLUE crab at Wally World. My human went running out to get some. But the only crab squeakies she could find were ORANGE.

She brought back three of these little ORANGE crabs, along with four lavender frogs and five blue starfish, but she told me and my pack that we could have them because ORANGE crabs weren't what was wanted by her human friends. My pack and I split them up between us, but I picked the ORANGE crabs as my own. They smelled delightful and made a most satisfying sound when I bit them.

Then my human got to clicky-clacking on that black thing at her desk and somehow decides that the ORANGE thing was what everyone wanted, and—you're not going to believe this, but—she took away my three toys.

Well, I didn't think that was right, so I wormed my way past the gate into the living room and quietly jumped up on the bench around the fire place. From there I pushed my way past the stereo on the counter top in the kitchen to reach the package of ORANGE crabs. I was just about to reclaim MY property when my human caught me and took them away again.

Her excuse was and is that if enough are collected, one will be included in the welcome bags at this big dog show, and since I'm going, I can get one then. Well, my kind are known for their intelligence and analytical abilities, so I've found another way to get what I want. I've written a little jingle and sent it along to all my human's friends asking that they all go crabbing for those delightful little ORANGE things. I figure if they will all collect enough, I'll have more than my share in a bag at this big show. If they find enough, my human might just decide to return MY three to me before the big show. Just to be sure my project is on everyone's mind, I wrote a little jingle for them to sing along to the tune of *Climb Every Mountain*. It goes like this:

Crash every Wally World
Capture every Crab
To make sure Puff gets his Orange Thingie!
Don't let one miss your grab!

What do you think? Am I a smart cookie or what? Do you think I'll manage to get my three little orange crabs back soon?
Jean C. Keating photo.

My Love/Hate Relationship with Arthur
By Puff, the Papillon

"What are you doing on my desk, Puff? You know you're not allowed on my keyboard!"

"Of course, I get up on the desk! How else can I make certain to clean up all the food crumbs you leave," I respond. Jean doesn't hear me, naturally. She's nice but dumb. I speak dog, cat, and English in addition to body languages of canine, feline, and human. Jean misses most of the communications that go on around here, poor thing.

She stumbles back to her desk chair, juggling an overfilled cup of coffee heavily laced with Splenda® and CoffeeMate®. A huge dollop of the mixture splatters down the front of her fuzzy pink robe. I quickly move my pristine, white fluffy tail out of the way as she tries to deposit the wet rim of the cup on the thirstystone cup rest and fuss at the same time. Did I mention she's not too good at multitasking!

"What are you doing, you silly brat?" She tries to push me away from the target of my efforts.

"Trying to remove this insulting figure of an Airedale,

of course. Whatever were you thinking to allow this in our home?" Try as I may, I just can't train my human to understand dog, so I continue to use body language on her, renewing my efforts to chew the head off this bronze likeness of an Airedale which she has afforded pride of place on her desk.

An Airedale mind you! When she knows—I mean her memory can't be that bad—that we members of the Astra gang do NOT tolerate Airedales! I mean, really! Did the Hatfields allow a statue of the McCoys in their mountain cabin!

"Come on, Brat. Get off my desk and leave my trophy alone. What are you thinking, trying to turn my Arthur into a snack? Don't you know I'm very proud of that national award for my book? Besides, you're going to crack a tooth!"

"Is not your book. I wrote it! Spent hours and hours on the floor at your feet with my head on your toe

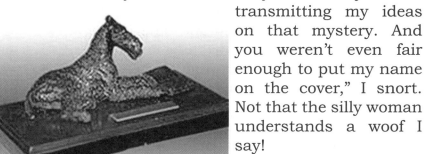

transmitting my ideas on that mystery. And you weren't even fair enough to put my name on the cover," I snort. Not that the silly woman understands a woof I say!

A sticky hand catches me off guard, grabs me and puts me on the floor. But I'm fast. I bounce back into her lap and on to the desk before she can blink twice. But I'm not stupid. I do accept the wisdom of Jean's caution in one respect. This bronze thing is one tough cookie to bite. So I settle for lifting my leg on the thing to register my antagonism.

"Puff, what in the world is your problem? One, that isn't nice. Two," now Jean is laughing at me, "you're wearing your parlor pants and trying to mark that award as yours is only going to get you diaper rash!"

"I am not trying to claim this as mine. Perhaps you've forgotten the Airedale that charged great great grandmother at her first show in Raleigh," I woof at Jean in disgust. Not that I think she'll ever learn to understand my language. "If you try hard, you might, just might, remember that the Airedale wanted to show his terrier qualities to a judge by attacking a seemingly helpless little Papillon puppy. Hee. Hee. Grandmother from-the-past sure showed him!"

Her screaming charge at him in response to his behavior brought the house down, the vet running from six rings away and the Airedale cringing behind his handler's back. In case you've forgotten, I haven't. And I'm sure this statue must represent that dog's fifth cousin, twenty-sixth removed or whatever. It's still an Airedale and my sworn enemy".

The annoying white blob on the other side of the desk starts its awful racket again, and Jean puts the coffee down to pick up the thing and stop it jangling. Thank heavens. All that noise hurts my ears.

"Hi. How's your morning going?" The low level grumbling that comes through the white thing mingles with the sounds Jean makes as she pauses to slurp liquid from her rapidly cooling coffee cup.

"Oh, not much. I'm just getting started on my overdue article and having a minor disagreement with my muse here. For some reason, he's decided that the figure of Dandy on my Arthur award should be replaced, probably by a likeness to him. You know Papillons. Never a dull moment!"

"Humans! See. I told you. She never listens to a thing I say."

Jean C. Keating photos.

North to Alaska

When I announced that I was going alone to Alaska (Anchorage), my decades younger friend responded with horror, "Not by yourself, at your age! How will you get around with a handicap walker?"

"Well, I can't go any younger!" I responded, choosing to be obtuse.

I have to admit getting there was not half the fun. Airline seats have shrunk—I refuse to admit to expanding with the years—and old bones stiffen more easily than they did on flights in my younger days to Hilo, Sidney, Tokyo, and New Delhi. The heavy duty Tylenol might have helped if I'd packed them in my purse instead of the suitcase somewhere in the cargo hold of the plane. I was in real pain after six hours in flight on the second leg of my trip when the pilot chirped that a beautiful view of Denali was visible peaking above the clouds at approximately the two o'clock position off the right side of the plane.

"As if anyone could tell a snow capped mountain from all the other white fluffy stuff stretched as a solid blanket below the wing tip," I grumped to myself. My slow brain struggled to remember that Mt. McKinley, my school day's name of America's highest point, was now renamed Denali, a word in the ancient Athabascan language of the region meaning 'the high one.'

Then the Boeing 757 slipped through a billowy blanket of marshmallows to reveal a golden world. I forgot about trying for a visual of the tallest peak in the United States! As far as I could see, trees and scrub were brilliant in the golden colors of the fall. Said fall is apparently a brief but gloriously exquisite span of the few weeks which separates a flower-filled summer from the heavy snows and dark of Alaska's long winter. Gold under the ground drew the original rush of settlers and adventurers to Alaska; the gold of the fall landscape on land reflected in the waterways around Anchorage and gave me the feeling we were settling on to an earth that was covered in that bright sparkling metal.

Since 40% of the population of this beautiful state lives in or near Anchorage, I'd expected Ted Stevens Anchorage International Airport to be the generic expanse of corridors flanked on two sides with food and small sundry vendors. Surprise! When I staggered into the main lobby trying to get the cramps out of my feet and knees, my reward was an unexpected sight. An unbroken expanse of glass along the entire side of the airport gave an unrestricted view of the Chugach Mountains, the lower slopes gray in late afternoon shadows and the snow-covered tops of the seemingly endless parade of peaks flashing a brilliant white in bright sunlight.

If the sight of my handicap walker on the luggage turnstile was foreign to the natives and visitors coming to fish, hike or hunt, so to me were the numerous ice chests secured with duct tape and holding who-knows-what of fishing gear which were as numerous as the suitcases. The jacket I'd felt stupid dragging through the Richmond airport in ninety degree heat and oppressive humidity felt wonderful in the brisk chill of early fall outside the Anchorage airport as I awaited a taxi for my

$23 dollar ride to the Anchorage Hilton.

In side by side lighted glass cases in the lobby, a polar bear and a brown bear were displayed, reared on their hind legs with massive jaws open to reveal impressive dentals. I'd always assumed from pictures and from seeing the two at separate times in zoos that the polar was the larger, but the two stood eye-to-eye. The more massive hindquarters of the brown poised over back feet that were smaller than those of the polar who needs a broader foot to move on the ice. The head and neck of the polar looked almost delicate compared with the blockier and heavier upper shoulders, neck and head of the brown.

The dining area of the Hooper Bay Café was separated from the lobby by a half wall, so I enjoyed my view of these large carnivores and an early dinner at the same time. Beer battered wild halibut and chips were a delightfully moist and satisfying treat after the sad excuse for a sandwich I'd purchased and consumed on the plane. A long flight, the four-hour time difference, and the thought of the cozy feather nest in my room was too much of a temptation to ignore so I charged my meal to the wrong room and retired to rest up for the next day's adventure.

Later, the phone awakened me from dreams in which I was trying to argue with two very large bears about who had the longer claws. My friend, fellow writer and professional photographer Carol had gone to the wrong Hilton—who knew there were two in Anchorage. She asked me to call and authorize the desk to give her a key to my room. I did! I asked them to give her the key to the room down the hall, the same one I'd charged my dinner to earlier. Carol and the desk got it straight; I went back to sleep and never learned what the guest in the other room thought of my bumbling.

By 5:00 a.m. the next morning, we were both up and

ready for a day of adventure. I'd been sleeping hard—except for my arguments with bears—for about ten hours. Coffee, fruit and omelets with smoked salmon and mushrooms warmed us for a chilly drive in light rain.

With full light, the rain stopped as the Seward highway carried us south out of Anchorage toward Resurrection Bay and a six hour tour of the Kenai Fjords. The shining gray ribbon of road was sheltered from the rising sun on our left by the tree covered peaks of the Chugash range, while the snow peaks of the Aleutian Range across Cook Inlet were brilliant. Pencil-thin evergreens rose like clusters of green pipe cleaners between numerous waterfalls that dripped down the side of the mountain, their lower branches extending little further than the top ones, since they must withstand heavy and long-lasting snows.

Midway to the boat dock, the road turned due east. Each bend of the road along the waterway now named Twenty Mile River brought another breathtaking view of mountains, low lying clouds and tinkling waterfalls. A turnout at the intersection of the roadway with Glacier creek afforded us a photographic opportunity to capture a glimpse of the morning's beauty.

Another car pulled in behind us, and the three young men who exited it started unloading hunting gear.

Randy Monrean, Jeff Regmart, and Justin Green patiently answered my nonsensical questions and explained that they were going off to hunt mountain goats. What they didn't explain, thinking that any fool should know, was that they needed to get to the boat dock, which Carol and I were blocking with our car. I wandered back toward our car asking Carol to take this picture and that. Finally, one of the guys politely asked if they might get to the dock to launch their boat. Okay! So I'm not a hunter! Especially an Alaskan hunter! Who knew that you needed to launch a boat beneath a sign about salmon fishing to go mountain goat hunting! Considering the bullet marks on this sign, I'm still a little concerned about what people shoot in Alaska; maybe dumb old ladies who block boat docks!

We made it to Seward in plenty of time to have tea in a little café and drool over the soft beige scarves, hats, and gloves made from the qiviut shed by musk oxen, called oomingwak (bearded ones) by Alaska's native people. Warmer than sheep wool and softer than the choicest cashmere, this soft underwool of the animals is shed in the spring. The knitted items made from qiviut were feather light and a great temptation.

But prices were too high for me to justify ($175 for a small scarf), especially since Virginia winters are just not cold enough to need it. Patiently dodging a huge Alaskan husky who was sauntering down the middle of the main street of Seward, Carol and I made our way to the Small Boat Harbor. We were pleasantly surprised to find a handicapped parking place at the front door so we pulled into it, unloaded my handicapped wheels and hurried to the front counter to get our tickets for the Kenai Fjord Tour.

"You'll have to move your car," the attendant at the counter directed. "That's a 30 minute parking place and the cruise lasts six hours."

"Okay," I respond. "Well, where is your handicapped parking place so I can leave my car during the cruise?"

"We don't have one," the attendant responded. The perplexed look on her face conveyed the unspoken, "Why would this be needed?"

Fortunately Carol and I were prepared for this reaction, for we were fast learning that Alaska was NOT a place

to which the elderly retired and not a place often visited by the physically challenged. Nationally franchised businesses had the federally mandated parking accommodations for handicapped; regional grown businesses did not. It wasn't lack of compassion, but a lack of perception that such would be of any use.

Only the hardiest souls winter here through the long

dark and deep snows. Most summer visitors come to hike, fish and hunt. I rolled myself down the long ramp to the dock in front of the Aialik Voyager, the huge catamaran which would take us out to see the delights of the waters out of Seward.

Other passengers gathered on the dock in front of the impressive boat looked a bit stunned at the sight of an old lady wheeling her walker to join their party, but quickly smiled and waved me to the head of the line to board the boat. Happily, a sturdy ramp was positioned to the lower level and two smiling assistants helped get my walker over the lip of the door frame. The best view of things was going to be from the upper deck, which could only be reached by a steep set of stairs, so with the gracious assistance of the two attendants, I was soon settled on the upper deck by a large window. The hardier souls of our afternoon group took up seats in the outside air of the boat's stern and came inside only for the lunch which was served shortly after we cleared the dock.

In bright sunlight Captain Tim Fleming skillfully maneuvered our white floating palace away from the docks at Seward and out into Resurrection Bay, all the while entertaining us with stories about the area and the trip ahead.

I was surrounded by large expanses of glass on four sides and overwhelmed with the majestic play of sunlight on sheer cliffs, blue green waters and white foam churned up by the powerful catamaran. It was easy to see why Secretary of State William Seward considered his 7.2 million dollar deal with Russia for

the cession of Alaska to the United States in 1867 to have been his greatest achievement. While detractors stupidly called Alaska Mr. Seward's Ice Box, those of us privileged to enjoy its beauty some 140 years later can be thankful to him for his astute foresight and to the people of Alaska for working so hard to preserve the pristine natural beauty of their state.

While my fellow passengers collected their lunches from the galley, one of the delightful staff brought me a tray with tasty wild haddock, sauce, a roll, a drink and an apple. Liza Lobe stayed to talk and to insure that I could have seconds if I chose. My stomach is rarely happy on water, so I stuck with one helping, but enjoyed getting to know Liza, a delightful Alaskan who just happened to have been born in Hampton, Virginia. She spends her Northern Hemisphere summers in Alaska as guide and crew of Kenai Fjord's boats and her Northern

Hemisphere winters (which are Southern Hemisphere summers) as a radio operator at Antarctica. Now how's that for an exciting life!

Lisa gave me a delightful running commentary of the sights we were passing when Captain Tim was busy negotiating the swells and bumps as the Bay flowed into the Gulf of Alaska. Our beautiful floating home varied its movement from fast forward to slow motion, one minute leaping along over the turbulent currents in the gulf and the next creeping past flat brown rocks, 20 feet away from playful Dall sea lions sunning themselves. Camera flashers were dutifully turned off so that we not disturb the sea lions whose numbers have diminished by 80% over the last 25 years. With the bright sunlight reflecting off our boat, I'm not certain that camera flashes would have been noted. Certainly the two young sea lions arguing in the picture did not seem to note our passing. A third young male, just out of the picture, certainly did, however. Indecisive as to which of the sparring pair to support, he turned instead toward our quietly passing boat and snarled a challenge to the catamaran. May he mate and breed many more brave souls like himself!

By this time in late September, many Alaskan birds have migrated south, so we were pleased to spot an immature puffin in the water. Captain Tim carried on a humorous debate with himself over the mike while easing the boat closer to the bird so that eager viewers and camera fiends could get a picture. He concluded that this was a young horned puffin that had lost the brilliant orange-yellow beak. By the time Carol got a clear shot, the little rascal did an underwater dive and we were left with a photograph of a water spout which we laughingly referred to for the rest of our trip as The Last of the Puffins.

As we eased around Aialik Cape and cruised up along the western side of Aialik Peninsula, the smell of freshly baked chocolate chip cookies enticed our noses. I was soon enjoying the warm treat, the chocolate still soft and running down my fingers while the blue green waters around me gradually became dotted with increasingly larger pieces of ice.

Chunks the size of railroad cars floated past as I tried to clean the sticky sweet off my hands. Our boat slowed and then eased to within one hundred yards of the mile-wide Aialik Glacier. Captain Tim cut the boat motor and the squeaking and moaning of the slow moving glacier was the only sound to be heard in the still air. Harbor seals sunned themselves on one of the largest of the ice flows, relaxed in the sun and safe from Orcas, because the water depth at the end of this bay is too shallow to support the beautiful black and white killer whales which are sea lions' natural enemies.

Across the front face of the glacier, the differing densities of the ice crystals soaked up red and yellow light, so that only blue light was reflected back in places. The result was a modern painting on brilliant white canvas of bright blue patches and ripples that rivaled Picasso.

When we eased out of the ice flow and headed back along the eastern side of the Harris Peninsula, Captain Tim was joined on the bridge by Ellen Burkowski, binoculars in hand and on alert for orcas and for the elusive humpback whales.

"I think most of the humpbacks have migrated south," Captain Tim warned, "except for one juvenile named Zipper. I call him Wonder Lung, however, because he can stay submerged so long."

True to the warning, we never did spot Mr. Zipper, but a pod of orcas entertained us for an extended period as we slowly negotiated the waters beside Bear Glacier. Ellen explained that orcas live 70-80 years, always remaining or returning to the pod into which they are born and led by a female.

The pod which surrounded our boat was labeled the AB pod and had been studied since 1983. Regrettably, this pod was impacted so badly by the Exxon Valdez oil spill that no calf has been spotted with the pod since 1989. They thrilled us with leaps and synchronized swimming displays till they tired of the game and went off in search of more food.

We slowed to enjoy sea otters at play in the waters and to watch the leaping antics of Dall porpoises. It is a testament to the care and consideration given to the native wildlife by this tour boat company that the sea creatures seem to regard the huge catamaran as just another natural inhabitant of the area.

Many of the fellow passengers were friendly and proud residents of the area like Joann and Kirk McKinley, who were celebrating their wedding anniversary with this afternoon cruise. In addition to entertaining me with delightful vignettes about life in this spectacularly beautiful region, they helped me to understand the typically Alaskan meaning of a word I was having trouble translating. Many residents talked of going outside for the winter months, which I finally came to understand was their term meaning to go to one of the lower 48 states.

It was hard to believe that six hours and 110 miles had flown by so rapidly, but the sun was low and setting when we eased back into the dock at Seward and Carol and I headed off to find dinner. I was still looking for my first moose, but hoping that we did not meet one up close and personal on the three-hour drive back to Anchorage. Road signs along the way warned motorists—of which we seemed to be the only one—to be wary of moose crossings in the same way signs warning of deer crossings are common along the Colonial Parkway between Williamsburg and Yorktown.

I never did see a moose wandering the streets of Anchorage, but managed to encounter three very tame ones at the Alaska Wildlife Conservation Center. I felt privileged to sit inside the car with the rain coming down hard and talk baby talk to an enormous wood bison placidly curled some 30 feet away with only a flimsy fence separating us. Wood bison were totally eliminated in Alaska in the early 1900's due to hunting, but a small group were obtained from the Yukon Territory of Canada and protected by the Alaska Department of Fish and Game in a so far successful attempt to reintroduce this largest land mammal to Alaska. The calf born at this preserve two summers ago was the first in Alaska in more than a hundred years. One of the six males in the group eyed me placidly, paying no attention to the black-billed magpie hopping around on his back and pecking at his skin to collect hairs and insects from his coat. This big fellow seemed to enjoy people-watching as much as I enjoyed the close view of him.

The next sunny day, Carol and I cut the writers conference again and drove north to the entrance of Denali State Park, which had closed for the season. An overlook near the park entrance afforded us an

unobstructed view of the majesty of this highest mountain in the United State. The pristine wilderness surrounding the peak, the stillness and lack of intrusion by man and civilization brought tears to my eyes with the thought that once all of America was this wild and lovely, before man ruined the air and the view with his presence. And I could but hope that the people of Alaska do a better job of preserving this natural beauty for future generations to see, breathe, and experience the wonders of its unspoiled grandeur.

My time in Alaska was way too short. How can I get back for a second visit with the least strain on my old bones? If traveling with my handicap walker raised eyebrows, I wonder what will happen when I show up with an electric scooter. I want to be there next May to see with my own eyes the wonder of the Aurora Borealis, the Northern Lights!

Carol Chapman photos.

85

Puff's Listening

My hearing aids are on the nightstand, but I know that any alarm from the smoke detectors during the night will bring an instant response from the tiny friend nestled beside me in the bed. Puff, my little six-pound Papillon, has been my hearing assist dog for more than six years, and has already acted swiftly to awaken me on another night when smoke filled the kitchen and I didn't hear the alarm.

His mother rejected him at birth. Feedings and care every two-hours of his early days produced an almost telepathic bond between us.

When I started to lose hearing in the high frequency ranges of sound some eight years ago, I struggled for a safe way to sustain my life style. I lived alone in my own home with my numerous Papillons. I wanted to continue doing so.

The answer seemed to be a service dog, so I searched the Internet for sources. The best options I could find were small dogs acquired from shelters and trained in at least three areas of hearing support. No idea of genetic background or breed was really known and the dog cost $14,000. Projection of actual active life was impossible.

I knew Puff's background for eleven generations of purebred Papillons. He was the seventh generation of my own breeding. And I knew he was especially bright for a breed that was already known as one of the ten most analytical of all purebreds. It required little intelligence on my part to have him privately trained as a hearing assist dog.

He swiftly and capably took over his duties as bed partner and living, breathing smoke alarm. I sometimes worried that his responses during our training MIGHT be somehow a response to some unintended signal from me since we were so closely bonded from his birth experience. My safety relied on his ability to act without a command or signal from me, to awaken me if the smoke alarm sounded.

I never meant to test his training. But aging brains sometimes get overworked by upsetting night-time phone calls. So it happened that I left a pot of soup simmering on the stove one night and went to bed without turning off the burner.

I awoke some time later with a very determined little blond and white dog standing on my chest and digging and tugging at my pajama top. The king sized comforter and sheet were on the floor, two button holes were torn and the buttons missing. A one-inch scratch mark on my left shoulder testified to the determined efforts of my tiny friend in getting my response. His training called for him to touch and keep touching me at the sound of the smoke alarm until I gave him his release word. His analytical talents translated his actions into scratching and digging me out of the covers when simple touching did not produce the desired response.

In the nearly seven years of his service as my hearing dog, he has not only insured my ability to safely continue to live independently but also provided delightful moments of pride and laughter. He goes with me to book signings and sits attentively on the table while we greet book buyers and visitors. One small child whispered to her mother after pausing to pet him and asking about the badge on his orange jacket that says HEARING DOG, "Mommie, can't all dogs hear?"

When another wide-eyed girl of about six reached to pet him, her older brother (by about a year) jerked her back by the back of her tee and corrected her loudly. "You're not supposed to pet him. He's a police dog!" I managed to contain my laughter—just barely—in the children's presence as I tried to imagine the diminutive size of the criminal who would be intimidated by my six and a half pound friend.

During a four day event at the Papillon National Specialty in 2009 I was a bit concerned when one gentleman stared at Puff for long spans of time over a three day period. I was about ready to approach him and inquire why he was so interested in my dog when he came over, and won my heart forever with the commentary: "Who trained that dog? I'm a trainer of hearing assist dogs for the Delta society and that's the best trained dog I've ever encountered." After that wonderful bit of praise, conversation flowed easily though I was horrified to learn from him that at that time, in May of 2009, the price of hearing dogs had exceeded $28,000 due to the high demands for such service animals by injured troops returning from Iraq and Afghanistan. Thankfully, internet searches today show that some sources now are using specially bred labs and Goldens for hearing dogs and offering those dogs free to those who qualify.

Admittedly, I'm grateful that my Puff is not one of those large breeds. As he pushes his tiny head against my paperback silently begging for a belly rub, he sprawls crosswise on the bed, but I still have room for myself and my book beneath the bedside reading lamp.

Despite my hearing handicap, I am safe and comfortable in my own home, confident that the small body who insists on sharing my pillow will guard us through the night from any threats of fire.

Jean C. Keating photos.

Shadow Warrior

"Ouch!" My screech was loud enough to awaken my neighbors in the house next door. "Drat it, Simba. That was my toe!"

My noisy response did little to faze the nineteen pounds of Maine Coon cat that had just flattened two of my toes with his bear-like paw. I recovered from my surprise in time to praise him for keeping the long, lethal weapons that served him as claws retracted.

I'm not certain where this large feline developed the habit of chasing shadows on the rug. But it delights me each night that my bedtime routine includes ten minutes of play with this reformed character.

He was eight years old when we first met. I was doing a book signing to support the Charlottesville SPCA. After six months of treatments for respiratory problems and adoption opportunities that had been unsuccessful, he was on his last day. I couldn't leave him there to be destroyed because all the adopters were taking younger felines. He distrusted humans and especially men who'd forced antibiotics into him during the six months of care, and so I became the frustrated staff to the Cat from Hell. Fortunately my dogs and my two old cats modified his behavior before I required too many stitches from his claws and teeth and I began to learn how to live with a Cat with Attitude.

He hissed at my small dogs that looked upon my two older cats as playmates. The only thing in the house that he respected from the start was my nine-pound, elderly female cat Misty. Misty's rules were simple: I eat first, you wait and take what I don't want, and you never get anywhere near my human's bed, especially the pillow on that bed.

I got tired of watching my little dogs being bullied in their own house. Scolding Simba about his behavior brought no improvement. When he started to push the dogs and my nineteen-year old male cat Sunny out of their favorite chairs and beds, I resorted to water and a spray bottle. Just to prove that you can teach an old cat (and an old woman) new tricks, we gradually modified our behavior to accommodate living under one roof. The little dogs went back to playing and sleeping intertwined with my two nineteen-year old cats and ignoring the Cat with Attitude. Simba gradually got tired of being ignored. He found that if he followed me around like the dogs did, he was not pushed away from the pack.

And suddenly I discovered that he was always sitting on the rug beside my bed whenever I went upstairs for the night.

The light from the bedside lamp made shadows on the rug, and the movement of my hands as I got ready for bed made shadow puppets on the rug. Simba pounced and joyfully pursued the shadows. The little dogs barked at his actions, at first, but gradually came to accept his antics. I was delighted to find that this unhappy waif, this difficult 'bad guy', took such pleasure in play.

As the months of our co-habitation stretched into our second year together, I found that he followed me about the house constantly, begging to be petted and acknowledged with no attempts at bullying or aggression. Complaints about hair pulling when I brush him were vocal now. The slashing claws were rarely seen, reserved for the rug on the bedroom floor and the shadow figures that tease him before returning to the safety of the space behind the bed's dust ruffle.

My big shadow warrior limits his energetic battles to engagements with silhouettes on the rug, and the rest of the pack has finally allowed him to join them on the bed at night. Misty even consented to sharing her prized pillow with him last week, although the rule about eating still holds.

That leaves me with only one problem. Does anyone know where you can get a bed larger than a California King?

Jean C. Keating photo.

Tiny Police Dog Seeks Lilliputian Criminal

I'm constantly surprised and delighted with the considerate and knowledgeable responses of people, especially children, to service animals. Being accompanied by one leads to some interesting conversations.

I have a hearing problem. Once I've removed my hearing aids at night and go to sleep I do not hear smoke alarms. So I travel with a service dog, a five and a half pound purebred Papillon named Puff who accompanies me everywhere during my day in a tiny orange vest with the standard patch saying SERVICE DOG DO NOT PET.

We recently went to Kentucky for a four-day book signing tour, so Puff was by my side in restaurants, parks and public places in addition to the book events.

At a Golden Corral, we were assisted through the line by smiling staff and the manager showed us to a table. When we came out to return to our car, an elderly man stopped me with the comment, "I didn't know dogs were allowed in that restaurant."

"Well, dogs aren't," I responded softly. "But service animals go anywhere their humans do."

"Oh," he returned. "Like that therapy dog in my wife's nursing home."

"Not exactly," I tried to explain. "Therapy dogs can only go where they provide the therapy, so they wouldn't be allowed in this restaurant. But a service dog goes everywhere with their human."

His age lined face registered his confusion and his response indicated I'd wasted my time trying to explain. "Next time I come, maybe I'll bring my little dog. She'd like the turkey."

I just smiled and silently prayed that the oldie wouldn't be too disappointed when he and his little dog were refused admittance.

Children, on the other hand, have no difficulty with the concept of a service animal and its difference from the rest of the animal kingdom even if sometimes it's a bit distorted.

Later that same day, Puff was sitting on the seat of my walker when I wheeled into the restroom at the Kentucky Horse Farm. A group of young children were coming out the same door. An adorable six-year old girl in the lead reached to pat Puff's tiny head. Her slightly older brother (I'd guess from the close resemblance) pull her back by her tee saying, "No, no. You're not supposed to pet him. He's a police dog!"

I managed to smile and contain my laughter as Puff and I continued through the door into the rest room area. A few minutes later in the safety of a stall, I chuckled softly while I whispered to my little hero, "We'll have to locate the Kingdom of Lilliput so you can find a criminal small enough for you to intimidate."

Jean C. Keating photo.

Trash to Treasure

At regular intervals during her first ten years of life, she was taken from the confining world of her wire crate and bred. In pain and loneliness she delivered her puppies, the only things that showed her love, only to have them taken from her side a few short weeks later. Then came the time she struggled in pain to bring forth her babies to no avail, and the only human hands she knew threw her out as trash.

Though she didn't know it, a long journey to a better life was beginning. In the gentle and loving care of Judy Hill, the dead puppies inside her were removed when she was spayed. She received her first dental care. And she got a name in place of a number. She'd come to Judy on March 17th, St. Patrick's Day, so Judy named her Erin. She ate well, objected weakly to the eye-drops which she continued to need, and sometimes joined the other resident Papillons on Judy's bed for the night. Thunderstorms frightened her, a characteristic often displayed by dogs who have been housed in outdoor crates.

Judy put Erin's picture and story on the web, and read through many wonderful applications from people interested in this little ten-year old. Finally she settled on a home in Hampton, Virginia with an industrial engineer and her nine-year old Pekinese. In route to this new home, little Erin flew with Judy from Kansas City to Dallas and finally to Orlando to attend PCA Nationals 2003, enjoyed the cheers and good wishes of the crowd at ringside as Judy carried her in the Rescue Parade, and traveled by van back to Virginia and her forever home.

In Florida, Judy stayed in touch via internet while the home visit was conducted and adoption details were documented. My fifteen-year old Papillon Ivory accompanied me for the site visit to Julie Owens and her resident nine-year old canine partner. Tiny, five-pound Ladye graciously showed Ivory the beautifully kept and shaded exercise yard off from the delightful sun room end of the house. She invited him to play and to share her bed, but he accepted Julie's invitation to share the sofa cushion beside me. I knew Julie and Ladye were special at first meeting. The confident and comfortable relationship was evident even before I learned that this nine-year old had been a cherished part of Julie's life since she was six-weeks old and had traveled with Julie to duty stations around the world. I've listened to too many lame excuses for getting rid of dogs when people's lives change and require more effort to maintain a relationship than the human partner is willing to expend. The strong bond between Julie and Ladye was obviously one for life; changes were something to be dealt with together. And this was the home that was waiting to welcome Erin.

At Nationals, Erin was held and entertained often by Barbara Foley of Newport News, Virginia, to get her comfortable with the next leg of her journey. At the end of Nationals, Judy wore sun glasses to hide her tears, as she bid goodbye to Erin and sent her on the trip back to Virginia from Florida with Barbara and the Keepsake pack. On the road trip north, Erin started the night loose in the living room of Barbara's camper, but another thunderstorm brought all the dogs including little Erin into Barbara's bed. Erin found the night a little easier to take from the safe haven under the covers sheltered in Barbara's arms.

Erin was wary and confused when Julie Owens and Ladye came to Barbara's home to get her and her extensive baggage of toys and goodies, for she had to say goodbye to yet another new found friend. She entered her forever home, found a quiet corner of the kitchen and curled up on a braided rug to await the next upheaval in her life. Two loving entities, one a remarkable little dog, undertook the job of making Erin feel welcome.

Julie took a week's vacation to stay at home and help Erin adjust to her new family. Ladye showed Erin where to go potty and stayed with her wherever Erin chose to be. This savvy and caring little Peke gave up her normal bedtime habit of sleeping in the bed with her adoring mistress to share the braided rug in the kitchen beside the lonely newcomer. When Julie came back from doing an errand on the second day of Erin's life with her, she was met at the front door by both little dogs that greeted her with happy body language and then raced to the back door to be let out.

Erin's bottom eyelid folded in on itself again, so

another trip to the vet and eye drops had to be endured. Even if she didn't care for the eye drops, Erin surely sensed the caring that surrounded her from her new family. Even her new neighbor came over each morning at 5:30 a.m. to help in holding her while Julie put the hated but needed eye drops in her bad eye.

By her fifth day in her new home, both Ladye and Erin had moved from the braided rug in the kitchen at night to Ladye's big lounge bed in the living room for sleeping. A particularly loud thunderstorm one night awakened Julie who found both dogs on the rug beside her bed, seeking comfort from their human. But Erin went back to the living room when the storm was over, and Ladye went back to stay with her new sister.

Erin now goes to sleep in Julie's lap, turns her belly up to be rubbed, and has gained a whole pound in the two short weeks she's been home. She is only a short hallway away from joining Julie in the big bed at night to sleep. Ladye will be glad to get back to her accustomed place among the soft feather pillows on the bed with her mistress and Erin will find a permanent haven of safety from thunderstorms and loneliness. What was once trash in now a treasured part of a loving family.

Jean C. Keating photo.

Tribute to a Legend

A legend walked into the Veterans ring at the 2005 National Papillon Specialty in Cincinnati and wrote an incredible addition to his magnificent career and to breed history. But then the 14+ year old CH Loteki Supernatural Being, known to dog lovers around the world as Kirby, has been doing incredible things all his life.

He first captivated the Papillon world as he flowed over the ring floor to a win at Papillon Nationals in 1994. In 1995, his perky personality came through the TV screens into American and international homes and made him an overnight hero to dog lovers everywhere when he became the first Papillon in history to win the Toy Group at the Westminster Kennel Club show. Reporters covering the 1995 Westminster show praised his effortlessly flowing gait, ring presence, proud and joyful head carriage, elegant neck, and beautifully expressive ears that fanned his heavy trailing fringes. They described him as being certainly the runner-up for Best in Show that year, if not a better choice for that prestigious award.

Kirby took his second and third Best in Specialty in 1996 and 1997. Then he more than fulfilled the accolades of Westminster reporters by becoming, during the 1998-1999 season, the only dog in history to win the triple crown of dogdom: Best in Show at The World Show, at the Royal Invitational (Canadian), and at Westminster.

Little wonder then, that he now adds two other firsts to his long list of record-setting achievements: the oldest Papillon to have ever won the National Specialty and the only Papillon to have done so four times.

Kirby's owner is John Oulton, a professional handler, who breeds papillons under the Cadaga prefix. He has loved, trained and shown Kirby during most of his awesome show career. When asked how he has kept this impressive and inspiring oldie in such top shape, both physically and mentally, Oulton said, "I've never stopped training him. He gets the same food, vitamins, and training as always. We walk a lot, and he leads the younger dogs, showing them how to walk and gait." Oulton also admits that he takes Kirby with him to any shows he attends as long as he doesn't have to fly. When asked if Kirby has any favorite doggie toys, Oulton said, "He likes any and all furry rats." It is clear that Kirby upholds the tradition of his breed as companion dog supreme, fulfilling his role as bed dog and pet, in addition to being an icon of conformation showing.

There's an old saying that "the apple doesn't fall far from the tree." Certainly legends like Kirby don't just happen; they are the product of careful breeding and development.

Lou Ann King, Kirby's breeder, was able to provide a valuable look at the background of this remarkable canine star. "Kirby's dam and sire brought both longevity and show potential to Kirby's makeup. His sire, CH Loteki Supercharger, a Papillon Club of America (PCA) Sire of Merit called Rico, lived to be fifteen and a half years old and traced his own lineage back to another PCA super star, Amer./Can. CH Jaclair's Doodles of Josandre CDX. Kirby's dam, CH Loteki Denzel Fortuneteller (Gypsy), was a second generation PCA Dam of Distinction." With the small litter sizes of the breed, a bitch that whelps 10 or more champions is rare; there are only twenty-six listed in the breed. Gypsy was the second generation in her line to do so, producing 10 conformation champions and one AUCH out of 13 live births. Gypsy, who lived to be fifteen years and nine months of age, also contributed longevity to the breeding.

One of Kirby's most impressive and incredible traits is his movement. He doesn't so much walk as glide across the floor. It has been described as 'big dog movement', and 'perfection in motion' by various judges and commentators. Possibly in years to come it will become known as 'Kirby movement'. It is certainly breathtaking to watch.

When asked to what she attributed such striking movement, King said, "Probably it comes more heavily from Gypsy's side. Gypsy has produced a daughter who is a third generation PCA Dam of Distinction and a granddaughter who is one champion short of being one.

PCA Nationals 2005 was blessed with hordes of beautiful dogs, and with Sandra Goose Allen, an elegant and highly qualified judge, one approved to judge all breeds and Best In Show. Allen had a softly rendered greeting for each of the entries as they were placed on the table to be examined. On the final day, she was poised in the center ring, elegantly attired with a sweet smile on her face, seemingly untouched by two previous days of ring work.

The veterans entered the ring to the heavy applause of the crowd at ringside. Each beautiful and precious oldie gaited around the ring, delighted to be back where they belonged, enjoying the adulation of the spectators. Kirby, with Oulton at his side, won his Veterans class and then Best Veteran Dog to enthusiastic cheers from his many fans.

The 77 beautiful Breed contenders (less a few absentees) filled the ring and the judge had the wonderful task of picking her choices from the graceful contenders. "I felt like a kid in a candy shop," Allen commented. "What an incredible sight! The classes were deep with quality. It was a breathtaking group of sound, happy Papillons presented with skill by their breeders, owners and handlers."

For the Breed judging, Allen divided first the dogs and then the bitches into groups of eight to ten, made preliminary cuts from each group and then brought her first cuts back into the ring for a second look.

Kirby returned with the first round cuts of champion dogs.

He entered the breed ring with Cheslie Pickett, a junior handler less than two years his senior, at the other end of his lead. A star in her own right, Cheslie has been showing dogs since the age of eight, finishing a grandson of Kirby's with three five-point majors before reaching her teens. At thirteen, she began showing in Junior Showmanship events. Her impressive list of first place wins in Junior Showmanship resulted in invitations to compete at the most recent Westminster and AKC Eukanuba Invitational. At Westminster in 2005, Kirby was often in her room and she proudly admitted, "He even slept on my bed one night during the Garden show."

Oulton returned to the ring handling another dog.

When asked why he switched, Oulton laughed and said, "I was trying to win with the younger dog." That younger dog was Kirby's son Nemo (CH Cadaga Civil Action, bred by Oulton and owned by Linda Sohn and Kyoko Ozeki), the top ranked Papillon in the United States for the past three years.

Cheslie is noted for her steady nerves and cool poise in the ring. When asked why he chose this young woman to handle Kirby in Breed, Oulton replied, "She has good hands, and Kirby likes her."

Cheslie shared a little bit of the inside instructions given to her in handling this icon. "John just told me to give him a long lead, keep up with him, and not hold him back." One cannot help but recall old stories about Kirby's distant ancestor, the famous Doodles, who was nicknamed 'the Clockwork Orange' because of the stories that handlers were only required to enter the ring to carry his number. Supposedly Doodles knew the commands and followed them by himself. Cheslie also indicated that "John gave me some tips on grooming him during the time we were in the ring." As things turned out, even Doodles would have experienced some need for help with the ring events.

For now began the drama, the beautiful and suspenseful dance that was to embellish this show and elevate a specialty breed judging to an academy awards presentation.

Sandra Goose Allen choreographed a suspenseful waltz with the select group of champions in the ring. Beginning with the class dogs, she sent the pair around the ring once with Winners Dog in front followed by Winners Bitch. Then she motioned the two to reverse the line up and sent them around the ring a second time with Winners Bitch leading the pair. Returning the class animals to the line, she brought out Best Veterans

Dog and Best Veterans Bitch for another two circles of the ring with first one and then the other leading the way. Then pairing off a champion dog with a champion bitch, she repeated the process. Veteran handlers were jumping to understand and follow her instructions. Cheslie was cool and unruffled by it all.

Allen was asked when she decided to do the "Waltz of the Dogs" in the ring. She replied, "I had it in my mind from the beginning. With so many spectacular dogs, I though it would be a good way to showcase them. It is entertaining for those watching but also gives the dogs a chance to show themselves off!" How very true! The performance delighted the spectators, confused the handlers a bit, but the four-legged competitors in the ring took it all in stride, with flashing ears and wagging tails.

This waltz "...also gives me a chance to match the dogs to the bitches," Allen said. "It helps me to see how they move together. The best of opposite has to complement the breed winner. This is a good way to evaluate my final choices." It gave those around the ring an opportunity to applaud each pair separately and the pairs of dogs responded to the extra attention with more enthusiastic posing as they gaited around the ring.

Allen followed the waltz with a second cut of her choices which did NOT include Kirby and directed the remaining dogs to circle the ring and exit. Just before Kirby and Cheslie reached the exit, she waved the two back in line in the ring, placing them behind Winners Bitch. It appeared to be an afterthought.

She then proceeded to gait and to evaluate the remaining champions in the ring, except for Kirby. To many outside the ring, she appeared to have forgotten Kirby was there.

When asked what her view had been from inside the

ring at this point, Cheslie responded, "I thought we had lost."

When Allen was asked when she decided on Kirby as the Specialty winner, she responded, "I was enchanted with him from the beginning in the Veterans Class. I always knew he was there. How could I miss him? If only dogs half his age could move the way he moves! I want to know what fountain of youth he is drinking from because he does not look like a fourteen-year-old."

When Allen finally revealed her choice of Kirby as Best of Specialty, it brought the house down, brought cheering crowds to their feet with tears running down their faces. "My God," exclaimed one spectator. "She was choosing her Best of Opposite and the five Awards of Merit all this time. And she fooled us all!"

A kaleidoscope of images sharply defines this dramatic close to the 2005 Papillon National Specialty:

* The dazzling smile that broke through the normally professional face of sixteen-year-old Cheslie Pickett as she realized she and Kirby had won, making her the youngest handler to ever win the Papillon National Specialty

* Oulton and Nemo in the center of the ring, too overcome with emotion to take their place with the other Award of Merit winners, tears wetting even Oulton's cheeks as he realized this oldie that he owns and loves had done the unbelievable

* Nemo jumping for joy, mistaking Oulton's excitement ...even above the crowd's roar of appreciation and approval, Oulton's words to Kirby's excited son, "You didn't win, boy."

* The cheering, screaming crowd around the ring ... on their feet, tears of joy and wonder making most faces shine brightly in the lights of the ballroom, realizing finally the exciting misdirection they'd enjoyed

* The beautiful smile of satisfaction on Sandra Goose Allen's face at the crowd's appreciation for her entertaining and beautifully conceived, directed, and produced suspense-filled drama...

* And at the center of it all, a dog named Kirby

Allen wrote in her critique of the show, "My Best of Breed winner is a fourteen-plus-year-old legend who has not lost the exceptional quality that helped him win over the years. He brought tears to my eyes. I was honored to have him in my ring!"

All who saw him felt honored to have been present at this history making event. According to Oulton, there are two large banners on display at Madison Square Garden that feature pictures of this incredible champion. As well there should be.

He has certainly lived up to the name given him so many years ago. King knew what she was doing when she named him a Supernatural Being.

Jean C. Keating photo.